D1485711

THE DEATH OF JUDE HILL

A PLAY BY RICHARD CONLON

Non-fiction section by Christopher Edge

Heinemann

Part of Pearson

Heinemann is an imprint of Pearson Education Limited, Edinburgh Gate, Harlow,
Essex, CM20 2JE.

www.pearsonschoolsandfecolleges.co.uk

Heinemann is a registered trademark of Pearson Education Limited

Text © Richard Conlon 2011
Non-fiction text © Christopher Edge
Typeset by Kamae Design
Cover design by Craft Design

The rights of Richard Conlon and Christopher Edge to be identified as authors of
this work have been asserted by them in accordance with the Copyright, Designs
and Patents Act 1988.

First published 2011

14 13 12 11 10
10 9 8 7 6 5 4 3 2 1

British Library Cataloguing in Publication Data
A catalogue record for this book is available from the British Library

ISBN 978 0 435 04609 5

Printed in Henry Ling, UK

Acknowledgements

We would like to thank the following school and students for their invaluable
help in the development and trialling of this book:

Little Heath School, Reading:

Marcus Baker, Joshua Baptiste, Chloe Bartlett, Callum Cartwright, Damon Crofts,
Bailey Curtis, Marcus Gallaghue, Joshua Morton, Leon Pearson, Lewis Scarrotts,
Zoe Vernon – Adams and Matthew Walker.

For Rosalind, Polly, Sashia, Barney, Clementine and Algernon

Contents

Act 1

Scene 1 1

Scene 2 8

Scene 3 11

Scene 4 15

Scene 5 18

Scene 6 23

Scene 7 25

Scene 8 33

Scene 9 36

Scene 10 43

Scene 11 47

Act 2

Scene 1 56

Scene 2 72

Scene 3 75

Scene 4 87

Scene 5 92

Scene 6 95

Scene 7 98

Scene 8 101

Scene 9 106

Scene 10... 108

Scene 11... 116

Scene 12... 118

Non-fiction:

Crime Scene Investigation by Christopher Edge.......... 121

Cast list

DREW: Confident, easy-going and independent. Not very academic, short on concentration and often restless, but likeable.

NOEL: New in town. Anxious, hesitant and apprehensive, particularly in new situations. Doesn't like change or not 'having a plan'.

LEE: Bright and articulate, with a curious mind. Perhaps more interested in the world of books than the real world.

JORDAN: Free-spirited and relaxed. Sees the world as a playground to be explored without limits.

RYAN: Always on the look-out for making something out of any situation, often illegally.

JUDE HILL: Self-assured and optimistic by nature with a keen sense of duty.

FRITH: A loner. Suspicious of most people and their intentions. A plain speaker with no time for polite conversation.

COUNCILLOR: Eager to look good in the public's eyes, likes to be seen as a pillar of the community.

DREW'S MUM & DAD: Proud of Drew.

NOEL'S MUM & DAD: New in town. Concerned about Noel fitting in and making friends.

PC LONGMAN: Kind but cautious local police officer.

HEAD TEACHER: Calm and authoritative.

GRAVEDIGGER: A deep thinker who attempts to lift the spirits with a dark humour.

TV REPORTER: A concerned local broadcaster. The kind of person who brings us 'the news from where you are'.

PR PERSON: Slick, efficient and businesslike. Keen to make the best image possible.

PRESS 1 & 2: Local newspaper reporters.

The Death of Jude Hill

ACT ONE Scene One

Drew and Noel walk onstage, Drew leading. Drew stops, Noel stops. Drew walks, Noel walks. Drew stops again …

NOEL Where are we going?

DREW We're not going anywhere – *I'm* going.

NOEL Where are you going?

DREW I don't know! I haven't made a plan, you know. I haven't got a timetable of where I'm going to be and when. 5

NOEL (*sounding unsure*) I normally like a plan.

DREW Well, I don't. I've got enough people planning my life and timetabling me. I don't need to do it too – so now I'm just (*thinks*) 'wandering'. 10

NOEL (*confused*) Wandering?

DREW Yeah, just wandering … sauntering, not to anywhere particular, just to see what comes. I like wandering, it's a nice thing to do (*making a point*) *alone;*… 15

NOEL Or with a buddy?

1

DREW (*ignoring Noel*) I don't have to be home till later, and before you ask, no I don't know what time 'later' means. So until then, I'll just wander. Maybe along the canal. Maybe across the fields; it's nice to be out of town. 20

NOEL I like to walk across fields. And the canal is nice. You can't get lost on a canal, can you? It's nice and clear … there and back. (*getting out a mobile*) I'll text my mum to say I'll be late, but 25 I'm safe, 'wandering' with you.

DREW (*mocking*) Your buddy?

NOEL (*not getting the joke*) My buddy, yes.

DREW Listen (*mocking*) 'Know-all'?

NOEL I have been saying for two weeks, Drew, that 30 it's Noel – just 'No-el'.

DREW (*pointing, speaking very firmly*) And I have been telling you for the same two weeks, *No-el*, that there is a difference between me being 'a buddy' and us being buddies – don't you get 35 it?

NOEL No … I don't. If a teacher says that you're my buddy then you're my buddy. It seems very clear to me.

DREW (*throwing up his hands*) That's the thing! It is 40 clear! It's clear to everyone except you. A: I want to be your buddy. B: I have been told that I have to be your buddy. Same word – different meaning. And anyway, do you always do what teachers say? 45

NOEL Yes.

DREW (*disbelieving*) Really? Always?

NOEL Yes.

DREW (*still disbelieving*) You never break the rules?

NOEL No. 50

DREW Or even bend them …? (*doesn't wait for an answer*) Don't even answer that – I can guess. (*exasperated*) How did I end up being your buddy?

NOEL You see, you *are* my buddy! Look, I'm new and 55 it's hard being the new kid … there's so much to learn and take in.

DREW I kind of thought that the buddy thing would end when the school bell went though …

NOEL (*shaking his head*) The teacher didn't say that. 60

DREW The teacher didn't say a lot of things; the teacher didn't say a million things! The teacher didn't say 'but you don't need to share a plate at dinner time'.

NOEL Oh, I agree. I don't think we need to do that. 65

DREW (*driving the point home*) Of course we don't! And you don't need to hang around me after school; it's bad enough having it all day!

NOEL (*trying to explain*) But I'm new to the town too, not just the school. I have to learn where the 70 shops are, when the buses run, which roads lead to which other roads, which are the good places and which are the bad places. There is a lot to take in! Coming from a village to the town is hard. 75

DREW (*pretending to not understand*) It seems to me like lots of things are hard to you.

NOEL (*very earnestly*) Yes … they are.

> *A pause, Drew softens a little.*
>
> *Drew throws stones, Noel texts.*

NOEL (*as if it has just occurred to Noel*) Drew … don't you like me? 80

DREW (*trying to be kind*) It's not that I don't like you – I'm just not *like* you. You're (*trying to be polite*) different.

NOEL You don't need to only like people you're like, do you? 85

DREW Don't you?

NOEL And 'different' can be good, can't it?

DREW But you're weird.

NOEL Surely it's good that we're all different, that some of us are odd – (*as if he is remembering something*) it's sometimes the odd people who make a difference in life. Lots of important people were thought of as 'odd' in their day – we need 'odd'. 90

DREW Is it your mum that tells you that? 95

NOEL (*not getting Drew's meaning*) Yes.

DREW Well, there you go.

NOEL (*after a thought*) You're different.

DREW What? What are you talking about? *Different*? From who? 100

NOEL (*after a thought*) From me.

DREW Well, of course I am; everyone's different from you. It's normal to be different from you.

NOEL But you're different from lots of the others in our class too. 105

DREW Ah … that's because I don't *want* to be the same as them. I *choose* to be different.

NOEL So different can be good. (*looks satisfied with this announcement*)

DREW No, different is weird and weird is bad, 110
unless *you choose to be different* – then it's … different.

NOEL So maybe you are like me after all?

DREW (*irritated*) What? How do you work that out?

NOEL Because we're both not the same … 115

DREW As …?

NOEL … the others. Maybe that's right, eh? (*trying to sum it up*) Maybe we are different in different ways. (*gives it another go*) Maybe we are similarly different. Maybe we are – 120

DREW (*has had enough*) Look, shut up. You are doing my head in. Same … different … different … same! Just leave it. Don't ask stupid questions and don't say stupid stuff.

NOEL And then will you like me? 125

DREW No.

5

NOEL Will you dislike me less?

DREW No.

NOEL Then why should I? I mean, where's my …
reason to shut up? If I was going to shut up
and I knew that things might be better when
I did shut up, well, then that would be good,
but if – 13▪

DREW (*jumping in*) All right … all right I will dislike you
less if you shut up. Just a bit of quiet would be 13▪
nice, please, OK? I said OK!?

> *Noel has shut up.*

Like I said … you're weird. (*appreciating the
silence*) It's nice when it's quiet.

NOEL (*forgetting to keep quiet*) I like the quiet.
Sometimes noise makes me – (*a glare from* 14▪
Drew makes Noel shut up again)

DREW Listen … (*a pause*) It's never quiet in town,
not really. There's always the ring road, or a
car horn, or some alarm going off. Sometimes
it's nice to have noise – I like all that, I do, but 14▪
every now and then it's nice to listen to –

> *They both look around as if they have just heard
> something.*

Did you hear that?

NOEL (*scared*) It didn't sound good.

DREW (*excited*) No, not good.

NOEL (*turning*) We should go back. 15▪

DREW What? Why?

NOEL Because it didn't sound good.

DREW You go back if you want. I'm going to see what that was – *because* it didn't sound good.

NOEL But what about me? If we're not wandering any more then I don't have a plan. What shall I do? 155

DREW A plan? Of course. I was forgetting. (*thinks*) Right, here's the plan –

NOEL (*relieved*) You have a plan? 160

DREW Yes, a plan. The plan is … we go and see what that noise was.

NOEL Why?

DREW Because it might have been something important. 165

NOEL Right, so we'll go and we'll see … And then?

DREW (*wanting to go*) And then – we'll see. And then we'll work out the next bit of the plan. OK?

NOEL (*relieved to have a plan*) OK!

DREW OK. Come on. 170

They exit.

7

Scene Two

Wasteland under a tall bridge. Noel and Drew enter to see Jude lying crumpled on the ground.

DREW & NOEL (*staying some distance away*) Oh my god.

NOEL (*turning to leave*) We should go.

DREW Don't be stupid. (*almost angrily*) We might be able to help.

NOEL I don't know if we can. I don't think we can. 5

DREW We might.

NOEL Look. (*they both look up*) That's a very big fall.

DREW (*squinting to see better*) What would anyone be doing up there?

NOEL What's up there? 10

DREW Just the old railway line. Hasn't been used for years. Not since my grandad was young.

NOEL (*turning to go*) I don't think we can help.

Jude makes a clearly painful small movement with a low moan.

DREW We can help.

NOEL But … 15

8

DREW (*looks around to prove his point*) No one else can!

> *They both move closer to the body. Drew crouches down and tries to hold Jude, who is a dead weight.*

(*to Jude*) Hey … you're still breathing, aren't you? You're still with us. You're just a little … but you're OK. Don't worry, you've just had a bit of a fall. But you're still with us, aren't you? That's good. I'm Drew and I'm going to stay with you and keep you safe until help gets here. 20

NOEL What help Drew?

DREW (*to Jude*) That's Noel. Noel is … my buddy. So 25 don't worry. You'll be all right.

NOEL (*beginning to panic*) I don't know if that's true, Drew. What's the plan, Drew?

DREW (*very calmly*) Noel is going to call for help now.

NOEL (*flustered*) Who will help, Drew? Who will help?

DREW (*irritated*) Ambulance! 999! That's the plan! 30 Ring, NOW!

NOEL Yes, right. Now … yes (*getting out his mobile phone*)

DREW (*to Jude*) We'll get you sorted and back on your feet. Just cuts and bruises, that's all. You'll be fine. 35

NOEL Reception! (*starts walking to find a clearer spot*)

DREW OK, just lie still. What happened to you, eh? What were you doing up there? (*looks closely*) I know you. I know your face. You went to my

9

school, didn't you? **40**

NOEL (*walks further away, calling back*) I've got
reception!

DREW (*softly*) You won't remember me. You left just
as I came in. I'm good with faces, see? Help will
be here soon, so we'll just stay here, just as we
are, nice and calm and quiet. You try to keep **45**
still and … rest … yeah … You rest and we'll
just stay here until help comes.

> *A still, calm moment then … with sudden force,*
> *Jude pulls Drew's face close and whispers*
> *something in Drew's ear and falls back lifeless.*

Oh no! No. Please. No. (*silence and stillness*)
Jude … that's your name. Jude. That was your
name. I remember … see? **50**

NOEL (*returning speaking really fast*) I made the call. I
got reception, I got through. I told them where
we were. I told them who I was and what we
heard and what we saw. And they asked me
all sorts of things, and I told them everything **55**
and they said they would be here soon and to
keep my phone on, and they would – (*sees the*
scene)

DREW (*sadly*) It's too late.

NOEL What do you mean, Drew … 'too late'? What's **60**
too late? Too late for what?

DREW Too late for anything, for everything. Too late
for Jude.

Scene Three

*At the police station, Noel and Drew sit, centre. PC
Longman and the boys' parents stand
around them.*

PC LONGMAN And are you sure that that is everything that
happened, just how it happened?

NOEL'S MUM Listen, officer, they've been through this already.

DREW'S MUM They've had a terrible shock. 5

NOEL'S DAD They've told you everything they know.

DREW'S DAD We really need to get these kids home.

NOEL'S MUM They need rest, they need to sleep.

PC LONGMAN As long as they're sure there's nothing else that
they think could help us in our investigations. 10

DREW (*thinking through the situation*) I was here …

NOEL And I was here …

DREW And Jude was lying right here.

NOEL (*remembering what they saw*) Yes, that's where
Jude was. 15

DREW And then Jude was (*can't say the word*) … gone.

NOEL It was horrible.

11

| PC LONGMAN | (*kindly*) OK, you lot get on home. But if anything occurs to you, at any time at all, no matter how small it seems to you, just call the station and let us know. OK? | 20 |

DREW OK.

NOEL Yes, we will.

PC LONGMAN And, Drew …

DREW Yes? 25

PC LONGMAN If you have any new thoughts on what Jude said to you –

DREW'S MUM Drew has already said it didn't mean anything, didn't make sense.

PC LONGMAN I know, I know. 30

DREW'S DAD So what more is there to say?

NOEL'S MUM These two have already been through so much today…

PC LONGMAN Sometimes, a night of reflection or a couple of days of thinking about it … well, things can get clearer in the mind. So if you have any new thoughts … 35

DREW'S MUM We'll call you.

The PC leaves them alone.

NOEL (*still shocked*) It was horrible.

NOEL'S MUM I know, love. (*gives Noel a hug*) 40

DREW We heard it first.

DREW'S MUM Yes, you said.

NOEL And then we ran toward it.

NOEL'S DAD You did the right thing.

DREW (*as if they are being doubted*) There was nothing   45
we could do.

DREW'S DAD You did everything you could. (*ruffling Drew's hair*) You did good.

NOEL We didn't know what to do for the best.

DREW It was horrible.   50

NOEL'S MUM (*trying to lighten the tone*) So this is the famous
Drew, *the buddy*. It's nice to meet you, (*to the parents*) all of you.

DREW'S MUM And this is Noel – we've (*slightly uneasily*) heard
a lot about you.   55

NOEL'S MUM Noel really appreciates having a 'buddy'. These
first weeks can be so hard.

DREW'S MUM And this has been awful for them.

NOEL'S MUM I can't imagine.

A slightly awkward pause.

DREW'S DAD (*to Drew*) We should get you home.   60

NOEL'S DAD Yes, it's late. Let's get you in the car.

They are about to leave in different directions.

NOEL Drew?

DREW What?

NOEL Do you want to come round to my house
tomorrow?   65

DREW Your house?

DREW'S MUM I'm not sure if Drew will be up to –

NOEL Or we could just … (*tries to think of the word*) wander?

DREW No. Your house … yeah, I'll come round … 70 that'll be the plan. That will be … nice.

Stillness, as all parents look surprised.

Scene Four

Music. The TV reporter faces straight out to the audience.

TV REPORTER   A shock discovery was made yesterday
evening at the base of the old railway bridge
in wasteland at the edge of the Kings Heath
Estate. Eighteen-year-old Jude Hill was still
alive when two local school pupils arrived on   5
the scene. Sadly, Jude was pronounced dead
in the ambulance on the way to Accident and
Emergency. The head teacher of Jude's old
school issued this statement …

HEAD TEACHER   (*speaking, as if to camera, clearly very moved*)   10
We're all so deeply shocked. Jude was such
a well-liked student and seemed to have so
much to live for. I can barely believe that this
was a case of suicide. I know Jude had many
friends who would have been only too keen to   15
help if asked. Jude had only recently started a
new job and was hoping to join the RAF. That
had always been Jude's dream, to be a flyer. I
can't believe Jude is gone; we feel such a loss,

and our thoughts go out to his family at this terrible time. 20

TV REPORTER Former sports-personality and local business leader Councillor William Matravers had recently taken Jude on as an office assistant and had this to say … 25

COUNCILLOR (*speaking to camera*) Jude was a very complex character: on the surface, bright and optimistic, but there was some anxiety there too. Jude had come to me and talked of not quite being able to see a clear future. 30 I tried to help, of course – my background in competitive sports has helped me to help others – but one is never sure how deep these feelings go. All those who work at my office are deeply saddened and shocked that we 35 were unable to do more. We knew Jude for just a few months and in that time we tried to help that young life towards the future it so clearly deserved, but one can never know what goes on in the depths of the human heart. 40

TV REPORTER Many messages of condolence have been left on Jude's Facebook page. It is indeed hard to judge from his page that this was a young life so near its end. The local police commended the two pupils for their prompt action. 45

PC LONGMAN (*speaking to camera*) We have no way of knowing how long poor Jude may have been under the bridge. Clearly the jump was meant

to end it all instantly, so we can only hope
his suffering was short. The two pupils did   50
exactly the right thing: they called 999 and
they stayed on the scene, despite it being a
deeply distressing incident. A young person
taking their own life is always a tragedy – to be
discovered while still alive by passers-by only   55
makes a terrible situation even worse.

TV REPORTER Councillor Matravers has established a fund in
Jude Hill's name to which people can donate
money.

COUNCILLOR I, and those I work with, just wanted to   60
do *something*. We know that money isn't
the answer, but perhaps we can make a
donation to a charity for young people or an
organisation that can offer hope and advice for
the next young person who feels as bleak and   65
as sad as poor Jude obviously did. All cheques
can be sent to me at my office in the high
street.

TV REPORTER The Hill family would like to extend their
thanks to all those who have expressed their   70
deep sadness at their terrible loss.

  Music.

Scene Five

The head teacher stands centre, at a lectern, in an assembly hall.

HEAD TEACHER (*starts by reading from notes*) The events at the end of last week have shocked us all. Many of you knew Jude and his family. Jude was so well liked by so many people that it will take a long time to come to terms with these tragic events. The school has lost a valuable ex-pupil, one who will now never grow to adulthood, will never join the RAF and become the pilot he always wanted to be. (*dabs an eye with a tissue*) 5

There is not much to cheer us in this story, not much to give us hope or strength. However, perhaps the fact that we have two current pupils who had the strength to stay and help, to call for assistance and to be there for Jude's last moments … perhaps that is something we can all draw comfort from. (*steps away and speaks without notes*) They did not turn their backs; they did not run. They were examples 15

to us all, examples of the best that we can be. 20
So in the middle of all this sadness, there is
perhaps something we can be a little proud
of too.

(*sadly*) Now … quietly … off to your classes.

Head teacher exits.

NOEL (*running up to Drew*) Have you been thinking 25
about it? What you told me when you came
round to mine?

DREW (*looking frustrated*) It's *all* I've been
thinking about.

NOEL But it still doesn't make any sense. 30

DREW It's just nonsense. But it was said, well, it was
whispered, as if it really meant something.

NOEL The police didn't know what it meant?

DREW Because it doesn't *mean* anything, but it
should, I reckon it should. 35

LEE (*approaching*) What doesn't? What should?

DREW (*to Lee, irritated*) What's it to do with you?

NOEL This is Lee.

DREW (*pointing out the obvious*) I know Lee! I have
been at this school for a bit longer then you, 40
you know. (*pulling Noel aside and speaking
quietly*) And in all that time me and Lee haven't
exactly been 'buddies'.

NOEL I thought Lee might be able to –

DREW To what? 45

NOEL To help.

DREW (*to Noel*) Do I look like I need help?

NOEL (*flatly, honestly*) Well… yes, actually. (*Drew frowns at Noel*) Lee is very good with words and things like that … 50

LEE (*calling out to Drew*) Look, if you don't want me around, that's OK.

DREW (*coldly*) OK.

LEE OK. (*Lee is about to leave*)

NOEL But the words, Drew, the words. 55

DREW I'll work it out.

NOEL (*blurting it out to Lee, who is walking away*) Drew thinks that the last words Jude said might mean something.

DREW (*giving Noel a dirty look*) It's nothing, I'll figure it 60 out.

NOEL (*getting frustrated*) But they don't seem to mean anything.

LEE (*turning, thinking*) The news didn't say anything about last words. 65

DREW Because they don't mean anything.

LEE (*after giving it serious thought*) I'd try and mean something if I thought it might be the last thing I said!

NOEL (*imagining it*) So would I. 70

DREW (*crossly*) I said, I'll figure it out.

LEE An outside eye might help.

DREW (*rudely*) An outside eye?

LEE Well, you know what I mean. An 'outside ear'
then.   75

NOEL That's what we need.

LEE It might be a stupid question … but why does
it matter so much?

NOEL Drew thinks –

DREW Drew doesn't think anything, OK!   80

LEE (*suddenly grasping what they are hinting at*) You
don't think that this is –

NOEL (*excitedly*) That's *exactly* what Drew thinks!

LEE That it isn't just a case of …?

NOEL It could be though, couldn't it?   85

LEE But the police don't think so.

DREW The police didn't look into that face; *I* did. The
police weren't there; *I* was.

NOEL (*not wanting to be excluded*) So was I.

DREW And I don't think Jude looked like a person   90
who had just jumped.

LEE But that means …!

NOEL We know! We know!

DREW (*a sudden decision*) Right … (*to Lee*) You're on.
You think you can help then; let's see if this   95
'outside ear' is any use. (*gives a quick look
around*) But not here. (*to Noel*) Back at yours
after school?

21

LEE (*disappointed*) Oh … I normally have homework club after school today. 10

DREW (***with a shrug***) Right … OK … Well, we're not going to force you. It's your call. Homework club or … (***with real meaning***) help solve a murder!

LEE (***almost in shock***) *'Help … solve … a …'?* I'll meet you at the front gates as soon as the bell goes. 10

DREW And not a word, not a single word, to anyone about any of this.

LEE Not a word.

Scene Six

A reprise of the TV music from before.

TV REPORTER   And, finally, as the funeral of Jude Hill draws
to a close, we can now talk to his former
employer, Councillor Matravers, who has
set up a charitable fund in Jude's memory.
Councillor, how has the public responded to   5
your request for support for this new fund?

COUNCILLOR   Well, among all this bad news, I am at least
pleased to say that we are generating a very
substantial amount of money, which will be
put to good use for young people across the   10
county.

TV REPORTER   And is it true that your business is also making
a donation to the fund?

COUNCILLOR   It's always difficult to talk about money at a
time like this and, of course, we don't want   15
to gain any public profile off the back of such
a sad story, but we are *of course*, as a local
business, putting our hands in our pockets
too. In fact, I make a pledge here and now

23

that whatever is donated by the public over 20
the next month will be matched, pound for
pound, by my company.

TV REPORTER That's a very generous offer, and one which I
suspect will help keep the money rolling in.

COUNCILLOR It seems the least we can do … in the 25
circumstances. If I thought it would
help I would raffle off my Olympic and
Commonwealth medals, but I'm not sure those
old things are worth much these days.

TV REPORTER Councillor, thank you very much. 30

COUNCILLOR Thank you.

TV REPORTER And, now, the sport and weather.

Music.

Scene Seven

Drew, Noel and Lee are in Noel's bedroom.

DREW   Right, shut the door. Good. So, this is now our
situation room.

LEE   (*looking around*) *Situation room* – wow! I've
seen those on telly!

DREW   If we really want to look into this case then it's   5
all or nothing.

NOEL   (*puts a hand up*) 'All' from me!

DREW   Because this is serious stuff, and if I'm right
we'll be dealing with some serious people who
won't want us nosing around.   10

LEE   Isn't it the police's job to nose around?

DREW   As far as they're concerned this is all tied up.

NOEL   (*thinking what it would be called*) An 'open and
shut case'.

DREW   And we don't know who we can trust; we don't   15
know who's involved.

NOEL   How high up it goes.

LEE   (*looking quizzically at Drew*) I think maybe
you've been watching too much TV.

DREW Right, two things. First, there is no such thing 20
as too much TV.

LEE … OK.

DREW And, second, (*firmly*) if you don't want in –
there's the door.

LEE (*urgently*) I'm in. I'm in! 25

DREW I'm not messing around – crime-fighting isn't
for cowards.

LEE (*offended*) I'm not a coward!

DREW I didn't say you were!

NOEL (*suddenly realising*) Hey! We're a *crime-fighting* 30
duo.

DREW (*putting a hand on Noel's shoulder*) Yeah, you're
right, Noel. Maybe we are.

LEE Then what am I?

DREW You're the person who helps the crime- 35
fighting duo – you're … (*thinks*) Commissioner
Gordon.

LEE Oh right … so which one of you is the
sidekick?

NOEL (*proudly*) Neither of us is the sidekick; we're a 40
team.

DREW Which just proves that *you're the sidekick*.

NOEL (*deflated*) Oh.

DREW OK, are we ready?

NOEL Ready. 45

LEE (*thinks*) Hold on! There are three Charlie's Angels. We could be like –

DREW (*interrupting*) No. Just no.

LEE (*defensive*) OK, OK … ready.

Noel's mum is suddenly at the door.

NOEL'S MUM (*surprised at seeing others there*) Oh! Well, this is all very nice. What are you lot up to? 50

NOEL (*excited, about to tell all*) Well, actually, we were just beginning to try to –

DREW (*suddenly*) Homework … club.

NOEL'S MUM Oh, great. What homework are you doing? 55

DREW & LEE (*at the same time*) Maths/English.

NOEL'S MUM Well, that's lovely. Noel won't need much help with maths … will you? (*silence from Noel*) But it's safe to say that English is not your strong area, is it? 60

NOEL (*awkwardly*) No.

LEE I'm good at English.

NOEL'S MUM Well, we appreciate any help you can give, don't we, Noel?

NOEL (*again uncomfortable*) Yes. 65

NOEL'S MUM But if there's one thing Noel is hot on it's computers. Software, hardware, uploads, downloads, fixes, cheats, patches, glitches – so if you need any help there –

27

LEE	(*pointing to Noel*) We know who to ask. 70
NOEL'S MUM	Good … right … Anyone staying for tea tonight?
DREW & LEE	(*at the same time*) Yes, please/No, thanks.
NOEL'S MUM	(*a little suspicious*) Well, I'll leave you to think on that one, but maybe some tea and biscuits will 75 help you get your brains going?
ALL THE BOYS	Yes, please.
NOEL'S MUM	Right. Good. At least you're all agreed on that. I'll pop to the shop and get something nice.

> *Noel's mum leaves.*

DREW	(*hissing the words out to Noel*) What were you 80 thinking? You nearly blew it there!
LEE	(*as if Noel is a fool*) You can't just tell people what we're doing here.
NOEL	I can't lie. I'm not sure why; never have been any good at it. Just can't do it. 85
LEE & DREW	(*disbelieving*) *You can't lie?*
NOEL	No.
DREW	Well, I'm glad we know that now, before you put your foot in it.
LEE	If you're in a crime-fighting duo, you just might 90 need to learn.
NOEL	Really?
DREW	Oh yes. We might have to break some rules to get to the bottom of this.
NOEL	Oh dear. 95

DREW Trust me, once you get used to it, you'll love it. But maybe for now, if people ask us questions … I'll do the talking.

LEE (*getting back to the issue*) So, these *last words* …?

DREW (*awkwardly*) Right, yeah. Now this is going to sound a bit …   100

LEE Just tell me.

DREW (*looks at Noel, then at Lee*) 'Day dealers'.

LEE (*confused*) 'Day dealers'?

NOEL Exactly … What does it mean?   105

LEE Dealing cards, dealing in business?

NOEL But 'day dealers' – so not at night, not in the evening? A shopkeeper?

LEE Are you sure it was 'day dealers'?

DREW (*with a shrug*) Almost sure.   110

NOEL 'Almost'? I thought you were sure?

DREW The more I think about it, the less sure I am. And it wasn't exactly clear.

LEE What else could it have been?

DREW I don't know … (*thinks*) Day … *dollars*?   115

NOEL Americans. It was Americans that did it … for dollars?

LEE What else could it sound like …? 'Day-dealers' … 'day-dollars'… 'daw-dlers'…

DREW (*staring at Lee*) 'Dawdlers'? What does that mean?   120

29

LEE   Someone who walks slowly, someone who *dawdles*.

DREW   Doesn't seem right.

NOEL   Maybe we were the dawdlers, maybe we didn't come quickly enough … maybe we *wandered* too slowly?

DREW   (*with a shake of the head*) I don't think so.

NOEL   Date-dealers?

LEE   Date-healers?

DREW   Date-heal-us?

LEE   OK, just give me a moment – give me some quiet. (*starts pacing*) Day dealers … date healers … day dollars … (*thinks*) Was it two words?

DREW   What do you mean?

LEE   Was it definitely two words or did it all run together?

DREW   It … I think … It all ran together.

LEE   (*as if saying something very important*) Daedalus?

NOEL   What's that?

DREW   (*with an intense look at Lee*) Say that again.

LEE   Daedalus.

NOEL   (*looking between the two*) What's 'Daedalus'?

DREW   (*suddenly excited*) That's it! That's what Jude said – but what does it mean? Is it French?

LEE   Greek.

NOEL   Greek?

LEE   Ancient Greek.

DREW   (*frowning*) Jude spoke ancient Greek?   155

LEE   We did this last year – Greek myths – don't you remember?

DREW   I might not (*a little embarrassed*) – I forget things sometimes.

LEE   Daedalus and Icarus.   160

DREW   (*with a click of the fingers*) Flying!

NOEL   (*also remembering something about it*) Wax wings!

LEE   Flew too close to the sun.

NOEL   I've heard of that.   165

LEE   Everyone's heard of it – it's pretty famous.

DREW   That was it. *Daedalus*.

LEE   But knowing what it means isn't enough.

NOEL   No.

DREW   What did it mean to Jude? That's the question.   170

NOEL   But don't forget what the police said.

LEE   What did they say?

NOEL   If you think of anything, let them know.

LEE   (*sadly, as if the excitement is over*) Maybe you should.   175

DREW   You think they'll believe us? You think they'll take us seriously? And what can we tell them? One word? One word when we don't even know what it means. No. We need more and we need to keep digging.   180

NOEL   Digging?

LEE   (*in a kindly manner*) Not real digging. Drew
means 'looking around' – hunting for clues.

NOEL   Where do we hunt?

DREW   Where do crime-fighting duos always hunt?   18

NOEL   (*confused*) Gotham City?

DREW   You are weird.

LEE   (*realising, and enjoying saying it*) The scene of
the crime!

DREW   *Exactly.*   19

Scene Eight

A gravedigger is filling in a grave.

GRAVEDIGGER Well, weren't you a popular one? Haven't seen
a bigger crowd in years. I'm not sure which is
sadder. The poor old dears who go into the
ground after all their friends have died, barely
a soul in the church, the occasional sniffle or   5
polite silence – or the ones like you. But you
filled the place to the rafters with real feelings
and tears. Real loss. (*a pause*) Sometimes I
wonder if I'm cut out for this job.
(*notices a man at the edge of the stage*) All right?   10
Are you here for this one? If you are, you're a bit
late. (*noticing the joke*) Eh … late! They're all late
here … (*no response*) I say … late. Never mind.
Do come and pay your respects if you want to.
I have my job to do, but you do what you like.   15

> *Frith enters slowly and suspiciously, limping and
> looking around.*

Did you know this one then? I don't know
which is more cruel. To die young and fit and

33

full of hope and plans, or to live so long that everything is behind you, with nothing to look forward to, your best years far behind you. What do you think?

FRITH (*gruffly*) Me? I don't know. I'm not sure.

GRAVEDIGGER (*almost casually*) Like one of the mourners said earlier: 'It's a crime.'

FRITH (*urgently*) What?

GRAVEDIGGER (*rephrasing the same statement*) It's *criminal* …

FRITH (*intensely*) 'Criminal'? What do you mean? What do they know?

GRAVEDIGGER (*defensive*) It's just a manner of speech, just a common phrase – they didn't mean anything by it. To be taken so young, it's just a crying shame, a waste. (*an awkward silence*) It was a lovely service if that matters to you. Lovely send off. Beautiful speeches, very emotional. I'd be happy with that when I go.

FRITH (*not listening*) What? Oh, good.

GRAVEDIGGER The vicar will be along in a minute. If you'd like a word, share a few thoughts, memories of the deceased, then I'm sure that will be fine. What with you having missed the funeral.

FRITH (*shooting a stern look at the gravedigger*) I didn't miss it.

GRAVEDIGGER Whatever. (*trying to look closely at Frith*) Like I say, the vicar is available to chat to if that helps you.

FRITH   (*turning aside*) Can't chat.

GRAVEDIGGER   OK, fair enough. Forgive me if I chunter on – I don't get much of a chance to chat in this line of work, you know how it is.

FRITH   (*preoccupied*) Can't stay. Must get on.   50

GRAVEDIGGER   No? Shame. Might help.

FRITH   (*distracted, almost rude*) I don't need help. Don't need to chat. Things to do. Must go. (*exits*)

GRAVEDIGGER   (*focusing on the work at hand*) Well, if you must. Leave me to my work. Don't mind me, I'll just   55 carry on with … (*looks up to see he is alone*) Funny one … I'll say that for this job, you meet all sorts. Not all sorts are the kind you'd want to meet though. (*finishing up*) There you go, all done, all tidy. That'll last you, that will. So   60 whatever else happened in your life, you can't say I didn't do right by you. Well, I'll be off then … Rest in peace, as they say. (*exits*)

Scene Nine

Drew and Jordan are up on the bridge, Noel and Lee down on the ground. Both Drew and Noel occasionally take photographs of what they see.

On the bridge.

JORDAN So what do you need me for? How come I get an invite to join the gang?

DREW It's not a gang; it's a team. A team that I am the head of.

JORDAN Fine by me. You won't find me trying to be the leader. I'm just happy to help … 5

DREW And, for a start, Noel or Lee wouldn't even think about coming up here, not this high.

JORDAN (*with a mock salute*) Ah. Well, I'm your man, boss.

DREW And, let's just say, I think you've got skills that might be useful to our … team. 10

JORDAN (*with a gently mocking smile*) Your crack squad?

DREW (*ignoring the dig, looking around*) If you like.

JORDAN So this is where it happened?

DREW Well, I guess up here is where it started, but down there is where it really happened. 15

JORDAN Then why aren't we down there?

DREW If there are clues to be found then they could be up here *or* down there.

JORDAN Right – we better start looking then. (*begins to look around then has a thought*) Actually, what are we looking for? 20

On the ground.

NOEL We're looking for anything … odd.

LEE Odd?

NOEL Anything out of place, anything that doesn't look like it belongs here. 25

LEE OK. (*after a quick glance*) I can't see anything.

NOEL But seeing isn't looking is it?

LEE (*frowning*) Isn't it?

NOEL Looking, really looking, takes time and patience. Like listening. 30

LEE Listening?

NOEL (*as if explaining the obvious*) It's different to hearing – listening is a skill.

LEE Is it? 35

NOEL It is.

LEE (*getting back to looking*) Drew's right – you are weird.

NOEL (*saddened*) Oh.

LEE (*with a slap on the back*) But that's OK – 'weird' can be good. 40

NOEL (*more upbeat*) Oh!

LEE Actually, just now, 'weird' might be very useful. Weird might be just what we need.

On the bridge.

JORDAN So if you found the body – 45

DREW (*turning to look at Jordan*) It wasn't a body when I found it. It was a person.

JORDAN Well, if you found … *Jude* down there … (*looking over the edge*) then the fall –

DREW Or the push. 50

JORDAN The whatever-it-was must have happened about here.

They start looking around.

DREW Nothing obvious.

JORDAN Looks like no one has been up here for years.

DREW (*standing up, looking further afield*) Maybe we're too close. 55

JORDAN Too close? What do you mean?

On the ground.

NOEL Sometimes to see things clearly, you need to step back.

LEE (*not sure what Noel means*) OK …? 60

NOEL Like if you were standing by a river, you'd know what that bit of river looked like, but not the whole thing.

LEE (*still not sure*) Right …

NOEL Like when you look at a map online – 65

LEE Like in 'Street View'?

NOEL Exactly! Street View gives you the detail, but not the whole picture.

LEE But if you zoom out –

NOEL You get the big picture – exactly! There are ways of seeing things. Different views will show you something different.   70

On the bridge.

JORDAN You're right – we needed to get back a bit. Look.

DREW I'm looking.

JORDAN There, the dirt …   75

DREW What about it?

JORDAN If you get the light behind it.

DREW (*squinting, focusing*) The moss on it is different in some places.

JORDAN It's been disturbed. It's the same in rock climbing – you can see where other people have gone up because things don't grow where hands and feet have been.   80

DREW It's been kicked around.

JORDAN Someone walked down here … from here.   85

DREW We know who – Jude must have walked down here.

JORDAN (*pointing to the ground*) But that doesn't account for two sets of tracks, does it?

DREW (*looking closely*) No … no, it doesn't.   90

On the ground.

LEE So if the body was (*pointing to a spot on the ground*) here …

NOEL Just here. I'll never forget it.

LEE Then the point where Jude went over the top must be … 95

NOEL (*pointing up*) Just there.

LEE What's … (*pointing too*) that?

NOEL Where?

LEE On the pillar, where the bricks go in – there's a ledge. 10

NOEL You're right, there's something catching the light.

LEE Something shiny.

The boys shout to each other.

DREW We've found two tracks! Two.

NOEL And we've found something odd. 10

DREW What is it?

LEE You tell us – you can see it better than we can.

NOEL Below you. On that ledge.

DREW (*looking over*) I see it.

JORDAN (*very casually*) I'll get it. 11

DREW (*as if it's impossible*) You'll never reach.

JORDAN I will if I hop down on to that bit there, where there's a line of stone sticking out. I'll brace my feet against that pillar, and that one, and then we'll be fine. (*hops over*) 11

NOEL   (*terrified for Jordan*) What are you doing?!

LEE   (*stepping back*) Are you mad?!

NOEL   (*waving wildly*) Get back!

DREW   (*calming them with a gesture*) Don't worry. I
told you Jordan had skills that might come in   120
useful. These are the skills.

LEE   Oh yeah. (*to Noel*) I think Jordan does rock
climbing …

NOEL   But don't you need ropes and helmets and
stuff? Not like this!   125

LEE   (*continuing*) … and parkour.

NOEL   (*looking from Jordan to Lee*) What's 'parkour'?

LEE   Can I explain later when I'm not waiting for
someone in my class to fall down a sheer wall
of brick and stone?   130

JORDAN   (*hopping back*) There you go. (*passes the find to
Drew*) It was just sitting on the ledge. Evidence.
Exhibit one.

DREW   Good to have you on the team! (*calling down*)
It's a piece of a phone! Must have broken on   135
the way down. Keep looking for the rest of it;
it must be down there somewhere!

NOEL   (*with a shrug*) It could be anywhere.

LEE   But, like you said, maybe we're too close.
(*calling up*) Can you see anything from up   140
there?

DREW   There's something in the bushes behind you.

JORDAN (*with a wave of the hand*) Behind you on the left.

NOEL (*trying to clarify*) Our left or your left?

DREW (*to Noel*) Your left. In fact, (*points*) it's behind the bushes.

JORDAN It's sitting there almost in plain sight.

DREW Lucky not many people come along here.

JORDAN (*quietly to Drew*) Why didn't the police find it?

DREW Because they're not looking for evidence. They're not looking for a murderer.

NOEL (*holding it up almost like a trophy*) I've got it!

LEE (*calling to Drew*) It's pretty busted up.

JORDAN (*to Drew*) Might not be any use.

DREW Yeah, (*calling down to Noel*) and it's been out in the rain and sun.

NOEL (*shouting to Drew*) It'll be fine.

DREW You sure? (*gives a little laugh*)

NOEL The SIM and memory cards are well protected; they're all we need. If there's anything important on here, I'll find it.

JORDAN Might take a lot of looking.

LEE (*shouting to Jordan, almost proudly*) 'Looking' is what Noel is good at: slow, detailed, boring looking. (*nudges Noel*) Because looking is different from seeing, isn't it?

DREW (*with a smile*) Well, what do you know? Looks like you've got skills too, buddy.

NOEL (*with a rare smile*) Thanks … buddy.

Scene Ten

The PR person and Councillor Matravers walk on stage and sit down, front.

PR PERSON   Thank you to all of you, ladies and gentlemen
of the press, TV, radio and, of course, the
public. We are here today to launch the
foundation set up in memory of Jude Hill.
The public has been very touched by this sad   5
story and have been very generous. A little
later we'll be announcing the full amount that
has been raised, the various charities that
will benefit from the money, and the way we
hope the project will develop over the next   10
few years. Before that point, are there any
questions from the floor?

PRESS
PERSON 1   (*raising a hand, then standing in the audience*) I'd
like to ask what role Jude Hill's family have had
in setting up the foundation?   15

COUNCILLOR   Perhaps I should answer this. We have tried
to extend what we hope is a hand of support
and friendship to the family, but at this terrible
time, when things are still so raw, so painful,

43

we hope what we have done is in the best 20
interests of the family, without taking away
from their grief while they reflect on their loss.

PRESS PERSON 2 (*standing, addressing the room, also from the audience*) I'd like to offer the support of our newspaper in making sure this issue stays 25
in the minds of the public. We believe that our young people need our support. We'll be covering the on-going work of young people's charities throughout the year with a special focus every anniversary of this terrible loss. 30

COUNCILLOR That is exactly the kind of action that this community needs to make sure people don't slip through the net. We need Jude to be the last young person in this town to have thought that there was nowhere to turn and no one to 35
talk to.

FRITH (*standing suddenly*) Can I ask a question?

PR PERSON (*politely*) And you are …?

FRITH (*glaring*) My name doesn't matter – I said, 'Can I ask a question?' Yes or no? 40

PR PERSON (*unsure, but still polite*) Well, yes, please do. The floor is yours. Feel free to –

FRITH (*interrupting*) Right. Good. What kind of people can ask for money from this 'fund'?

PR PERSON I'm sorry, I don't quite – 45

FRITH (*rudely*) What if someone – I'm not saying who – had somehow, over time, lost their way?

Found themselves doing things they regretted.
Do you think money would help them, to deal
with the bad thoughts, the images that go   50
through their head? Can money make any of
that better?

PR PERSON (*confused*) Who are we talking about here …?

FRITH (*through gritted teeth*) Like I said – I'm not
saying who.   55

PR PERSON (*still confused*) The funds are supposed to be for
helping young people –

FRITH (*interrupting*) We were all young once. What
happens to the young people we used to be,
eh?   60

COUNCILLOR (*curtly*) I don't think this is the time or place …
and perhaps you need to give some thought –

FRITH No. No. You're probably right. Not the time or
the place. I'll think about what is the time and
the place, I'll give that some thought.   65

PR PERSON Please, if you have nothing more to add to the
meeting –

FRITH (*interrupting*) Do you think what goes around,
comes around?

PR PERSON Maybe it would be best if we asked you,   70
politely, to –

FRITH 'Karma', they call it. Do you think that if you do
something bad then bad things come to you?

PR PERSON Who are we talking about here? What are we
talking about?   75

FRITH   (*almost muttering to himself*) Who and what, who and what? Good question, good question … but what's a good answer … eh?

PR PERSON   Maybe you should stay and we can –

FRITH   (*sharply*) No! Can't stay, shouldn't stay … must go, lots to think about. (*bustles out*)   80

COUNCILLOR   (*standing, watching Frith leave*) Some people have no respect, no sense of occasion. I think we can all agree that that outburst should not be covered in the press, in the interests of the family. (*agreement from the room*) Thank you. Now … back to business …   85

Scene Eleven

The boys are in the situation room.

JORDAN (*perusing the space*) So this is the – the – what did you call it?

DREW The situation room.

JORDAN Situation room – I love that.

DREW You might love it – but this is serious stuff.   5

JORDAN I can see it's serious, it looks just like it does in the movies. (*pointing out things*) Whiteboard, pictures of the victim and the scene. Times, dates, a map of the area, evidence bags, sticky notes with lines between them. Looks like   10 we're a proper crime-fighting team. Like the A-Team.

NOEL (*putting it politely*) Technically, this is a crime-fighting duo plus support.

JORDAN (*with a frown*) So I'm 'support'?   15

LEE (*looking to Jordan*) Yeah, and if I'm Commissioner Gordon, I have no idea what you are.

JORDAN (*with a laugh*) The butler?

47

NOEL (*very seriously*) Actually, the butler, Alfred, is really very useful. He plays a vital role in many plotlines.

JORDAN (*too cool to bother*) Listen, whatever … so what do we know? (*noticing a word on the board*) What's (*mispronouncing it*) Da – ed – alus?

DREW It's *Daedalus*. And we're not sure, but I think when we find out, it will unlock everything.

JORDAN (*nodding*) Cool.

NOEL OK. Let me just wake up the laptop. I think you'll find what I have discovered is very interesting. (*pointing things out on screen*) Some of the files were hard to access at first and there was lots to plough through; it seems that Jude never cleared out the outbox on that phone. And there were lots and lots of pictures, lots of short video clips. I have watched all of them … and I've read all of the texts and all of the replies – hundreds of them.

DREW (*looks amazed*) You went through *all* of them?

NOEL (*as if to prove a thorough job has been done*) Twice.

JORDAN Honestly?

LEE (*to Jordan*) You should know that Noel can't lie – if Noel says it, it's true.

JORDAN (*looking closely at Noel*) Weird.

NOEL Please, I didn't want to go through everything;

that would take all night, so I'll take us straight to what I think are the important items.

DREW We're all yours. (*sits*)

NOEL First, this set of texts.   50

LEE Who are they sent to?

NOEL The person is only named by initials … BM.

JORDAN BM?

LEE Doesn't get us very far?

DREW Unless we can link BM and Daedalus.   55

NOEL I've pulled out the texts to and from BM (*pointing to the screen*) here.

DREW (*reading as Jude*) 'Hi, I have discovered something that I think you might need to know about – can we chat about it soon?'   60

LEE (*reading as BM*) 'No problem, let's chat soon.'

NOEL You see it starts calmly enough. The next one is a few days later.

DREW 'Keep finding more and more things that don't make sense – need you to explain something.'   65

LEE 'Don't worry, we can sort this all out simply enough. Give me a week or so to look at this.'

NOEL (*Scrolling down the screen*) I wasn't sure at first if BM was helping or what. The next one is about ten days later.   70

DREW (*reading as Jude*) 'Something is really wrong here. I keep finding more bad stuff.'

LEE (*reading as BM*) 'If something wrong is going on

49

we'll get to the bottom of it together – don't talk
to anyone except me.' 75

DREW 'I really think I need to talk to someone about
what is going on – nothing seems to make sense.'

LEE 'I can deal with this – trust me. Let's meet and
talk it over.'

DREW 'I think we've found something really big. 80
Yes, let's meet – where?'

LEE 'I can explain everything, it will all come clear. See
you at 6 o'clock at –

LEE, JORDAN
& DREW '– the old railway bridge'.

NOEL And that's not all. (*clicking on the keyboard and* 85
sitting back to watch) Watch this.

A video plays on screen.

JUDE (*we see Jude walk so as to be in shot*) Hi Mum,
hi Dad. Now the first thing you need to do
is not panic when you get this. I'm fine, and
I promise I'm not involved in anything … 90
dodgy. But I have stumbled across something
that looks like it might be quite important and
dangerous. So I've decided that once I let the
police know what I know, it might be best if
I lie low for a couple of weeks. I promise I'm 95
safe and sound, but I can't tell you where I am
– otherwise you won't be safe either. (*putting
out a calming hand*) Sorry to be dramatic, there's
no need to panic. I'm fine. Don't bother telling
work that I won't be in, they'll know. (*trying to* 100
be upbeat) And if you don't hear from me for

a while it's because I'm OK, not because I'm not OK. Does that make sense? Anyway, all you need to know is that I'm doing something good, but certain people won't want me to do it – you'll be proud of me in the end. Maybe my name will even get in the papers. (*gets up, and sits back down*) Love you, speak soon and don't worry. Bye. (*gets up to turn the filming off*)   105

Silence.

JORDAN   (*open-mouthed*) Weird.   110

DREW   (*looking down*) Jude looks so … alive.

NOEL   And that was filmed on the phone we found less than two hours before the meeting on the bridge.

JORDAN   (*not getting it*) So Jude is not dead?   115

LEE   (*turning on Jordan*) What?!

DREW   Of course Jude is dead – we were there!

LEE   But Jude thought that the meeting on the bridge wasn't going to end the way it did. He trusted this BM person and he was planning to   120
blow the whistle on something big.

DREW   (*putting out his arms to indicate the scale*) Something really big.

JORDAN   (*realising, looking at Jude on the screen*) Oh! And he never got the chance to send it!   125

LEE   So 'BM' is our murderer. And we have a phone number – do we just ring it?

DREW   (*firmly*) No, we don't.

JORDAN   Why not? … Scared?

DREW   (*ignoring the last comment*) I thought of calling it, but then we just blow our cover. No. That number is useful and will be more useful later – I think we save it until the right moment.

LEE   I guess. Knowledge is power and all that.

DREW   (*with an air of satisfaction*) Imagine what they'll think when they get a text from Jude's phone!

JORDAN   Freaky.

NOEL   But BM could be anyone – we have no idea who they are at the moment.

LEE   No idea at all.

DREW   Until we can link Daedalus to this 'BM' … we're stuck.

JORDAN   And this is the list?

NOEL   (*pointing to something*) That's it, our 'Daedalus list'.

JORDAN   (*reading*) *Flight – flying – feathers – birds – fathers – sons.* (*turning to the team*) It wasn't Jude's dad, was it?!

LEE   Of course it wasn't!

JORDAN   (*reading*) *Too close to the sun – wax wings – science?*

LEE   Daedalus was a scientist, of sorts.

JORDAN   (*reading*) *Falling to earth –* (*reflects*) that's weird, that's what Jude did, isn't it? (*looks back*) *Flight – birds – falling to earth.* (*has a thought*) Have you ruled anyone out yet?

DREW We haven't ruled anyone *in* yet!

JORDAN (*turns to the group*) Do you know that weird person who lives in the fields behind where Jude's house is?   160

LEE (*intrigued*) What weird person?

NOEL (*looking around*) 'Weird' doesn't mean 'murderer', let's not forget.

DREW '*Lives in the fields*'?!

JORDAN Well, not actually in the fields, but the house   165 is pretty isolated. (*moves to look at the map on the board*) Here's Jude's house, and here's the wacko's house.

DREW (*getting excited*) Not far from the old bridge either.   170

NOEL (*trying to restore some sense*) What do you mean, 'wacko'?

JORDAN Wacko enough to make some kind of fuss at the press launch of that Jude Hill Foundation. My dad was there. (*turns to Noel*) He takes   175 pictures for the paper.

DREW Right …

JORDAN The house is a right state. Crumbling wreck of a place. Like a dump. My dad says he's a really anti-social kind of person.   180

DREW Loner?

LEE (*as if it's a lead*) Keeps himself to himself?

NOEL   Maybe he's just 'private'?

JORDAN   He takes in injured birds. Apparently his place is full of them. I've seen all sorts of people take birds up to that house.

DREW   Maybe he doesn't look after the birds at all!

LEE   Yeah, maybe he … you know … (*mimes wringing a neck*)

JORDAN   (*thinks*) And he walks with a limp. (*thinks some more*) Funny arm too, I think.

NOEL   (*trying to be firm*) Which, again, does not make this person a murderer!

JORDAN   (*as if producing more evidence*) My dad says he barely speaks either. He lives out there alone. (*looks quizzically at the team*) How can you not know about him?

DREW   And the name … What's his name?

JORDAN   That's the thing, I've never known his real name, just a sort of nickname we always used. (*a little ashamed*) It's not really very nice, um, I guess it's more a term of abuse really –

NOEL   (*with pen raised to write on the board*) So what do we call this anti-social, limping bird-lover then?

JORDAN   That's the thing (*takes the pen*) … from when I was little, we always just called him (*writes*) the Bird Man.

DREW   BM!

JORDAN   Exactly.

LEE   (*slapping his forehead*) Oh my god! And you can

see how we can connect that straight to Jude's last words, to Daedalus!

DREW (*pointing at the board*) Everything! Flight, wings, falling to earth. Bingo!

JORDAN It makes perfect sense.   215

DREW Now we're getting somewhere. (*looking at the map*) Right, BM, we're closing in on you.

LEE The net tightens.

DREW We've got you.

NOEL So now do we tell the police?   220

DREW No!

LEE Now we gather evidence.

DREW Now we pay a little visit to our animal lover, who doesn't seem to like people so much. (*draws a circle around the name on the board*)   225

JORDAN Now we do some breaking and entering. (*draws a circle around the house on the map*)

DREW Now we see what goes on behind the front door of the Bird Man. (*writes 'Murderer!' next to the name*)   230

ACT TWO Scene One

The team is hunched over, whispering outside Frith's house.

NOEL (*whispering, picking at his fingernails*) I'm not sure about this.

DREW You don't need to be sure about it – I'm the leader, and I'm sure and that's what matters. We follow the plan – OK? (*looking to the team for support*) 5

NOEL (*gesticulating desperately*) But this plan is *against the law*!

DREW Sometimes you have to do things that are a bit wrong to make something else right. 10

RYAN (*walking up to them, casually, confidently*) Actually, if what you're doing is to stop something even more serious happening then it's technically not against the law.

DREW (*to Ryan*) Bang on time. 15

NOEL (*whispering to Drew*) Who's that?

LEE You didn't say anything about anyone else!

JORDAN I thought we were the team: the squad.

DREW (*to Noel*) This is Ryan. Ryan used to be in our
class.   20

NOEL Used to be?

DREW Yeah. Ryan got … (*thinking*) What's the word,
Ryan?

RYAN 'Excluded', Drew. I got excluded.

NOEL (*to himself*) I'm really not sure about this.   25

DREW Ryan's on the team. Ryan can do things none
of us can.

JORDAN (*sarcastically*) Or none of us want to.

RYAN (*to Jordan*) Whatever. (*to Drew*) Right, shall we
crack on then?   30

LEE (*looking at Ryan, disbelieving*) But what you said
just then, about something not being illegal, is
that true?

RYAN Of course. I know the law.

NOEL I'm not sure.   35

RYAN What if you saw a house on fire, and there
were children crying upstairs?

LEE I'd call the fire brigade.

DREW (*puffing out his chest*) I'd go and save the
children.   40

JORDAN Me too.

RYAN Exactly. (*doing the actions with arms and legs*)
You can smash windows, break down the door
– as long as it's to save those kids, you can
break and enter that house.   45

LEE I guess.

RYAN So what we're doing is right, OK? (*looking to Noel*)

NOEL I do hope so – I'm a bit lost on what's right and wrong these days. 50

RYAN We solve a crime, we catch a murderer; *we're right*.

JORDAN We're heroes!

LEE Yes, but don't forget the law of 'joint enterprise' or 'common purpose', which says that even if 55 you don't actually do anything, like, for instance, the breaking and entering, but you are there as part of the group, it makes you just as guilty as the person who actually does the crime.

RYAN (*mocking*) Get *you*! 60

NOEL Is that true?

DREW (*to Noel*) We're not here to talk about laws; we're here to get the job done and solve the crime. (*to Ryan*) So you think you can get in?

RYAN (*really calm and confident*) This is no problem 65 for me. Looks like the doors and windows are pretty insecure. Not very tight fitting; I'm betting there's no window locks. Give me two minutes and we're in. (*goes round the side of the house*) 70

NOEL (*whispering*) I'm not sure what my mum would say if she knew I was with Ryan. Ryan is what she'd call a 'bad kid'.

DREW (*as if stating the obvious*) Ryan is a bad kid. That's why Ryan is useful. 75

LEE (*trying to make it simple*) Right now 'bad' is 'good'.

NOEL You see this is just the sort of thing that I'm no good at.

JORDAN You'll get used to it.

NOEL OK, if you say so. You're the boss. (*suddenly* 80 *panicky*) What if that Bird Man is in there?

DREW The lights are out so either nobody is home or there's someone sitting in the dark – not very likely.

LEE And what are we looking for? 85

DREW Anything.

JORDAN Anything?

DREW (*looking from one to the other*) Anything that links this Bird Man person to Jude. We get in, we look, we get out. 90

NOEL And do we all look in each room?

DREW Yes, we stay together. OK?

LEE, JORDAN & DREW OK.

Ryan opens the front door from the inside.

RYAN (*relaxed and casual*) Ha, told you! (*with a welcoming gesture*) Come on in. 95

DREW All OK?

RYAN It's a weird place; there are birds everywhere.

In cages, all over the place. And most of the windows are covered up so it's really dark.

JORDAN Told you … crazy. (*pointing to his own head and twirling his index finger to indicate 'mad'*)

LEE Hmm … suspicious.

DREW Let's go. (*steps towards the door, looks back to his team, nods*)

> *They enter.*

LEE It's weird. You can feel their eyes on you.

DREW It's well creepy.

JORDAN It smells like the zoo.

LEE Where are we? (*with hands out to feel his way*)

RYAN The front room I think …

JORDAN Torches on?

DREW (*with a hand signal, like a soldier*) OK, but keep them low and away from the windows.

> *They turn their torches on.*

JORDAN And try not to wake our feathered friends.

NOEL (*screwing up his nose*) I don't like birds.

RYAN Nor me.

NOEL Beady eyes … (*looking around*)

RYAN (*creating talons with his hand*) Sharp little claws …

NOEL (*with a shiver*) Pecky beaks.

JORDAN (*mocking*) Some country kid you must have made. I thought you were supposed to love all the little creatures.

NOEL   All the little creatures in the country end up on a plate in the town – that's what they're for!

Jordan laughs, a little too loud.

DREW   (*stopping, speaking urgently*) Can we just get on 125
with this? We've got a job to do – and we don't
know how long we've got!

RYAN   (*like a professional*) One of us should keep a
look out.

DREW   Good idea. (*pointing, by way of instruction*) Noel, 130
stay by the window.

NOEL   (*confused*) I can, but it's got newspaper all over it.

DREW   The front door then.

LEE   But keep it closed.

JORDAN   Look through the letterbox. 135

NOEL   And what if this if this limpy-murderer starts
coming up the path?

DREW   We scarper out the back – just stop asking
questions and look. You look, we look.

LEE   (*slowly, importantly*) Oh my god. 140

DREW   What?

LEE   Look!

NOEL   What?

LEE   Here!

JORDAN   Where?! 145

LEE   Here, on the wall – it's some kind of noticeboard.

They all gather by Lee.

NOEL (*from the back, trying to calm them*) Even crazy people have noticeboards.

LEE Not ones that are covered with pictures of Jude and bits from the paper. It's all about Jude. 15

DREW Oh my god.

RYAN (*slapping his forehead*) I've seen this in films. This is what killers do! They obsess about someone, they find out everything about them, they spend all their time planning how to kill them … 15

JORDAN There's probably writing on the wall too. That's what mad killers do, crazy stuff like that.

NOEL (*joins the other boys*) OK, *now* do we call the police? 16

A shuffling sound.

DREW (*an urgent whisper*) What was that?

NOEL (*more a moan than speech*) Oh … no …

LEE Was it you?

RYAN It wasn't me. 16

JORDAN It wasn't me.

DREW (*repeating the question*) What was that?!

NOEL (*again*) Oh … no …

A silence.

FRITH It was me.

The team shriek and turn their torches on the Bird Man who is sitting in a chair in the corner of the room.

FRITH (*calmly*) But that's not so strange is it? After all,   170
I do live here. It's my home. But you, you are –
what's the word – burglars? Would that do?

The team huddle together. Noel is now at the front.

NOEL We're going to die!

FRITH No. You're not going to die.

NOEL (*trying to back into the group*) We're going to be   175
tortured!

LEE (*also trying to hide*) In the basement! It's always
in the basement!!

Lee starts panicking very dramatically.

FRITH But you have been caught.

DREW (*with what is clearly fake bravado*) No. *You've*   180
been caught.

*Frith stands, turns on a bare ceiling light bulb,
looks around.*

FRITH And you, I'm guessing, are Drew?

NOEL (*slumping to his knees*) We are going to die!

FRITH And the one who keeps jabbering on is
probably Noel? Am I right?   185

NOEL (*head in hands*) Oh my god. I'll never see my
mum again!

Frith switches the lamp on behind him.

FRITH (*after looking carefully at the group*) You could
have just knocked, you know.

DREW (*accusing, pointing*) What were you doing,   190
sitting in the dark?

63

FRITH I like the dark, always have. It's amazing how your eyes adjust, the things you can see. And the birds like the dark, and I like the birds. And I am *allowed* to sit in the dark; sitting in the dark is not a crime. However, I think you'll find that breaking and entering is …

LEE (*bravely popping up and then backing down*) Not if it's to stop something worse happening!

DREW (*still defiant*) Were you waiting for us? How did you know we were coming? What are you going to do with us?

FRITH 'Do with you'? '*Do with you*'? You watch too much TV.

LEE (*putting a hand up*) I said that. I told you!

DREW You're not going to deny it?

FRITH (*confused*) Deny what?

LEE (*suddenly noticing*) Look, on the back of the door. That scarf, that was the same kind of scarf that Jude was wearing in the picture that was in the paper.

FRITH That's because it's *the scarf* that Jude was wearing in the picture in the paper. You can turn your torches off now, you know.

DREW So you can kill us?

FRITH You may not have noticed that there are five of you and one of me. I'm not so fast on my feet, not as strong as I was – I think you stand a better chance of murdering me. But that's not why you're here is it?

NOEL No!

FRITH So now that you are in my home, perhaps I should introduce myself?

DREW (*boldly*) We know who you are!

FRITH Oh, you know who I am …? So my name is …? 225

DREW (*confused*) Er … well, we don't … I mean, I didn't …

FRITH You don't know who I am, you only think you know. You think I'm, what is it? 'The Bird Man'?

JORDAN That's right. 230

The rest of the team shush Jordan.

FRITH It's OK, I know what they call me … 'The Crazy Vet', 'The Zoo Keeper' … I've had lots of names given to me. But they're not *said to me*, just whispered under the breath of the local kids – and the adults too. I've had it for years. But I do 235 have a name. My name is Frith, Cameron Frith. For you lot, 'Frith' will do.

DREW (*not sure where to go from here*) So …?

FRITH So nothing. How strange that you are here. Right place. Wrong reason. How easy it is 240 to jump to conclusions. You're just like the rest of the people in this town. (*turning away from them, looking around the room*) What am I? A loner? One of those people who keeps themselves to themselves? Live out here all by 245 myself? With all these birds? Walk with a limp? (*suddenly turning back*) *So what*? So I must be a

65

murderer? Please! If I was a murderer would I be nursing all these animals to health?

DREW (*with crumbling confidence*) So the pictures of Jude, the scarf?

FRITH (*walking over to the scarf, touching it for a moment*) Jude was here. Often. I liked Jude and, believe it or not, Jude liked me. And trust me, I don't have a great number of friends. Jude found a bird. (*walks over to a cage and brings out a bird*) This one actually.

NOEL (*backing away a little*) I don't like birds.

FRITH (*to the bird, with a gentle stroke*) Near dead, you were, weren't you? Another hour and you'd have been a goner. (*placing the bird back, turning to the team*) But Jude found this little one and brought him to me – and Jude didn't judge me on anything except my love for these birds. (*getting angrier, pacing*) Jude was good and kind. Jude didn't think the worst of me. (*facing them*) Not like you lot. (*turning and shouting at a blacked out window*) Not like the rest of this town!

DREW We're not like the rest of this town. We're the only five people actually trying to do something!

FRITH Maybe you're right. (*calming*) Jude came here for a couple of weeks over the summer. (*sitting*) Sat in this chair and drank my tea – confided in me sometimes too. We talked a lot, and I don't

talk to many people, or listen to many either.
But I listened to Jude, *(leaning towards the team,*
confidentially) Jude *told me things …*

NOEL *(almost to clarify the point)* So you didn't kill   280
Jude?

RYAN *(with disappointment)* So it was suicide?

NOEL Did Jude tell you about feeling down, feeling
like there was no one to turn to?

DREW I'm telling you – it wasn't suicide.   285

FRITH *Suicide*? *(angering)* That's what people think
now, that Jude was a suicide case? Rubbish!
Complete nonsense! *(getting up and grabbing*
a nearby newspaper) But if it's in the paper, it
must be true! *(throws it in on the floor grabs*   290
Drew by the shoulder, addresses the team) Drew's
right, Jude was never going to jump off that
bridge. Jude had everything to live for. Jude
had a bright future. RAF training all planned.
He was going to be a flyer by twenty-one. That   295
kid was going places. *(lets go of Drew's shoulder)*
But mark my words … *(quieter, conspiratorial,*
looking around) Jude *knew something*,
something big, which was supposed to remain
secret. And Jude was scared of something. Of   300
someone.

LEE Like in that video clip on Jude's phone!

JORDAN That's what Jude said.

NOEL Excuse me … *Frith. Who* was Jude scared of?

FRITH (*not answering*) So am I to understand that this, ³⁰ this *team*, is a crack crime-fighting squad.

LEE Technically it's a duo with three helpers.

DREW (*bravely*) And I'm the leader of the duo *and I know* that Jude was murdered.

FRITH (*coming up close to Drew*) And you found Jude ³¹ so you know that it was a push and not a jump – you feel it in your bones, don't you?

DREW (*sadly*) I saw it in Jude's face.

FRITH Of course. (*softens*) You've been through a lot over these past weeks. (*playfully*) *Almost* ³¹ enough to make me forgive you for jumping to stupid conclusions.

NOEL We found Jude's mobile phone. There were texts –

JORDAN To someone called BM. ³²

FRITH BM? (*under his breath*) Makes sense.

LEE We thought of you.

FRITH Me? (*confused for a moment then it becomes clear*) Oh yes … 'The Bird Man' – of course.

NOEL Sorry. ³²

FRITH Sometimes people see what they want to see, when actually the answer is staring them in the face, is right under their nose.

JORDAN And Jude's last word was 'Daedalus' so we thought about all this, and the birds … ³³

LEE Of flight.

FRITH (*thinking*) *Flight* … yes, of course. Interesting.

LEE Do you think you know who did it?

FRITH Oh, I know – and what's weird is I almost knew before it happened. I suppose I've been waiting for something like this to happen for a long time. But it's almost over. 335

DREW Really?

FRITH Really.

JORDAN What do you mean? 340

FRITH I mean that if you, (**turning to Drew**) Squad Leader, and your team have all the skills needed, we have a job to do.

JORDAN When?

FRITH Tonight. Now. *Carpe diem!* 345

LEE I know what that means!

RYAN (*whispers*) What does it mean?

LEE (*whispering back*) 'Seize the day'.

RYAN (*frustrated*) And what does *that* mean?

DREW (*excited, to the team*) It means we've got a job to do. (**to Frith**) Doesn't it … Frith? 350

FRITH (*toying with them*) Unless you have something better to do?

LEE No!

RYAN No! 355

FRITH Nice warm beds to go to?

JORDAN No!

DREW No!

NOEL Actually …

FRITH There are things that need doing that I can't do. An office that needs breaking into.

RYAN Great! That's me!

DREW We can do that!

FRITH Computer files that need, what's the word, 'hacking' into, and they'll be well hidden, I promise you that.

NOEL (*nervously*) That will probably be me …

DREW Yeah! We can do that.

FRITH Then you are quite a team.

RYAN Whose office?

NOEL Whose computer?

FRITH The killer's, of course.

RYAN Cool.

JORDAN You know how to get to the killer?

FRITH Isn't the saying … to find the killer, *follow the money*?

LEE (*confused*) Money?

NOEL Jude wasn't killed for money.

DREW Nothing was taken.

FRITH I'm talking about the kind of money a person would never carry on them, the kind of money you couldn't spend in a lifetime. I've had my suspicions since this nasty business began, but I didn't know how to go about proving it. You

seem to have come along to my door, just at 385
the right moment.

DREW And the killer? This 'BM'. The killer … is?

FRITH (*walking over to the wall of pictures*) Like I said
before … sometimes people see what they
want to see … 390

LEE When the answer is under our nose?

FRITH (*opening a penknife*) Right … (*sticks penknife in
an image of Matravers*) there.

DREW Jude's boss?

LEE Some councillor, isn't he? 395

JORDAN BM?

FRITH William Matravers – but known to his staff as …

ALL Bill.

FRITH (*pulling out the knife*) Sorry, Bill, old pal, time's
up. (*to the team, smiling*) Let's go. 400

Scene Two

On the street at night. Noel, Drew, Lee and Frith are looking up at a window of an office block.

NOEL (*alarmed*) They'll never get in that window. It's three storeys up.

DREW If Ryan follows Jordan then they'll get in it. Ryan can get into most buildings.

FRITH If they're supposed to be getting in over there   5
(*points*) then why are they going up over there
(*points to somewhere else*)?

DREW If I know Jordan they'll go from the big bins to the low flat roof. (*pointing them out*) Ah, here
we go …   10

LEE (*watching it happen*) Nice.

DREW Now they'll go from the flat roof to the ledge sticking out over there.

LEE No way.

DREW Way. (*the boys make noises of astonishment*) And,   15
now, from the ledge to the balcony up there.

NOEL (*as if it is clearly impossible*) I don't believe it!
(*after seeing it*) Oh my god! They did!

DREW (*laughs*) And now off the balcony and across the scaffolding, I reckon. 20

LEE (*as if it's not a big challenge*) I could do that.

DREW Up the pipe.

LEE (*looking up, as if it is a really big challenge*) I couldn't do that!

DREW And there you go! 25

NOEL (*looking from the climbers to Drew*) 'There you go' what?

FRITH (*irritated*) They've not only gone one floor too high, they're also on the wrong building!

DREW (*with a smile*) Just watch. 30

FRITH They wouldn't …

LEE I wouldn't …

NOEL Jordan would …

DREW Now for the jump.

> *They all watch open-mouthed.*

DREW (*to Frith*) So Jordan gets Ryan to the window, 35
Ryan gets in the window, lets us in and our
geeky genius here (*jokily pats Noel on the head*)
gets the files we need. How's that for a crime-
fighting squad?

FRITH We'll see. The job's not done yet. 40

LEE Hey, what do I do?

DREW (*not sure*) Er …

FRITH Maybe keep watch out here?

DREW   No, that would be you. (*hands Frith a phone*) Take this.   45

FRITH   (*recoiling*) I don't like those – I've never used one. Do I have to?

DREW   (*firmly*) Yes, you do. (*getting out another phone and calling Frith's*) We can keep in touch on this. You watch the street and we'll ask you   50 anything we need to know. (*answering Frith's phone and handing it back*) Just talk.

FRITH   (*into the phone*) OK.

DREW   Welcome to the twenty-first century.

FRITH   I'm still getting used to bits of the twentieth.   55

DREW   (*kindly puts his hand on Frith's shoulder*) You'll be fine.

   Jordan and Ryan arrive at the door of the office and open it.

JORDAN   (*buzzing with excitement*) That was fun.

RYAN   (*casually posed with the door wide open*) You coming in or what?   60

DREW   Wasn't there an alarm?

RYAN   (*almost offended*) Yeah, of course there was! What do you think I am, some kind of amateur?

NOEL   (*biting a lip and wringing hands*) Oh dear.   65

Scene Three

In the office, the team stare at a computer. Frith is acting as look out outside, still on the phone to Drew.

NOEL Are we sure this is the one?

DREW (*into the phone*) We're in Matravers's private office …

FRITH It will be on that computer – don't even look anywhere else. 5

LEE (*looking around the office*) BM … what have you done?

JORDAN Who would have thought? (*with a sad shake of the head*)

RYAN I wouldn't. 10

JORDAN (*shocked*) Jude's *boss*!

DREW (*trying to shake them out of a sombre mood*) So, Noel, come on! Fire this computer up and let's get those files.

Noel sits and starts to work.

LEE What if they've been deleted? 15

NOEL (*without looking up*) Unless you're very serious about it, or if your software is very special, then there is no such thing as deleting.

RYAN (*confused*) I thought you just pressed 'delete'.

NOEL (*very casually*) You can click it all you like and 20 of course it will go from the screen, but it's not actually gone, not really. Every PC holds the information of every document, every email, every site visited, every touch of every letter and number on the keyboard. It's all in there, 25 somewhere.

JORDAN (*disbelieving*) Really?

LEE Wow. Like a ghost in the machine?

NOEL You just need to know where to look.

RYAN (*frowning*) I hope my mum doesn't know where 30 to look.

NOEL (*looking up at Drew*) But first …

DREW What?

NOEL (*pointing at the screen*) We need to get past this.

RYAN The password … 35

DREW (*disappointed*) I thought you'd have a way of cracking that!

NOEL Sorry. (*trying to encourage them*) You get me in and I can find anything that's there, no matter where it is, but I need to get past this first. 40

DREW How about 'let me in'? That's a classic.

NOEL (*tries it*) Nothing. Keep thinking.

RYAN   12345?

NOEL   (*tries it*) No. Too simple.

JORDAN   Password? **45**

NOEL   (*tries it*) No.

RYAN   Try 'password' again, but put fives in place of the S's.

NOEL   (*tries it*) Nothing. And you do know, don't you, that you should never use any of these? **50**

DREW   (*laying down a challenge*) Come on, guys, Matravers already had Jude discover this stuff. He's not going to hide it behind some flimsy, useless password – think … think!

FRITH   Can you hear me? **55**

DREW   (*snapping*) What?

FRITH   If I might suggest … you need to stop thinking like crime-fighters and start thinking like a criminal.

DREW   (*more gently*) Good point. **60**

LEE   (*a flash of inspiration*) Hold on! I'm a genius. *This* is what I'm here for. For my mind, for my literary skills. Stand aside, watch me work. (*types*) D … A … E …

DREW   Daedalus. **65**

LEE   And … (*dramatically*) 'enter'!

NOEL   (*flatly*) Nothing.

LEE   (*disappointed*) Oh.

NOEL   Sorry.

LEE (*angry*) It has to be right. It makes sense.   70

NOEL Sorry.

LEE How can it be wrong? (*paces around*) I was so sure. That's not fair.

NOEL Any other suggestions? If not, we need to just clear out.   75

RYAN We could take the PC with us?

DREW (*patronising*) It would be nice for them *not to know* we had visited.

RYAN I guess.

JORDAN (*a sudden thought*) What about 'qwerty'?   80

NOEL (*tries it*) No.

RYAN 'Abcde'?

NOEL (*tries it*) Nothing – we're drawing a blank. It's got to be something more … more …

LEE WAIT! I have it. Of course. Forgive my earlier   85
lapse. This makes even more sense. It's perfect. Stand aside, watch me work … *again.* (*types*) I … C … A …

DREW Icarus.

JORDAN Of course.   90

DREW *That's* why you're here.

LEE It has to be. (*quietly, to himself*) Please work, please work. And 'enter'.

NOEL We're in!

The whole team cheer quietly and clap each other on the back.

FRITH Well done, team. Now crack on – crack on! 95

DREW Now look for 'Daedalus', anything with Daedalus.

NOEL (*suddenly authoritative*) Look, sorry, everyone, but if it's here, deleted or not, I will find it, but I will need silence. I need to think. I need to 100 concentrate. I need silence.

> *As one they are all silent. There is nothing but rapid tapping from Noel as the others watch intently, then a sudden sound as Noel's mobile rings out – the boys shriek.*

RYAN What's that?

NOEL It's OK, it's OK, it's me. It's my phone. It's a text!

RYAN At this time!

LEE From who? 105

NOEL (*looking at it*) Oh no. I'd rather not say.

RYAN (*casually*) Then lie.

LEE Noel can't lie.

RYAN (*looking closely at him*) You can't lie!

NOEL That's not a bad thing! 110

JORDAN Who's it from?

FRITH What's going on up there?

DREW We're OK – we're into the computer. Noel just needs to dig up the files.

NOEL (*blurting it out*) It's my mum, OK! My mum just 115 wants to know that I'm fine.

JORDAN At this time?

NOEL She worries.

LEE That's sweet.

JORDAN Text back that you were asleep.

NOEL *I can't lie.*

RYAN Then text back 'I am fine, goodnight'.

NOEL (*grumpily*) I am not *fine*! I have just broken into a building and now I am hacking into a computer. I am far from fine!

LEE How about 'Don't worry about me, goodnight'.

NOEL *I'm* worried about me. If she knew what was happening she'd be terrified!

RYAN (*puts a hand out*) Give it to me.

NOEL What!

RYAN (*barking the order*) Give!

NOEL (*caving in*) OK.

RYAN (*texting*) 'All fine here – sleep well, night-night'. There you go, and you didn't lie. I did. I can lie for England, and anyway, *everything is fine.*

DREW Right, come on, (*to Noel*) you, back to work. The rest of you, silent!

The only sound is tapping for a few seconds.

FRITH (*aware that he is breaking the silence*) You may need to know that there is a car coming up the street with security markings on it.

DREW (*turning away from Noel*) OK. Could be for any of the offices around here.

FRITH (*unsure*) Could be.

NOEL (*irritated*) Please! (*Drew is silent again. Noel starts working intently*) OK, Daedalus, where are you? 145 Look in the obvious places first, shall we? Here … or … here? (*clearly becoming gripped by the task*) No. OK. That's fine. So if I were to hide you, where would I do it? Where would I put you? (*manic tapping*) There maybe? (*pause*) No. 150 Or there? No. What about in … here? (*pause*) No? (*rubbing his hands together*) OK. If you want to play hard to get, that's fine.

The team step away from Noel to speak.

RYAN (*whispering*) Who is Noel talking to?

LEE (*whispering back*) The files. 155

DREW (*a little confused*) Noel doesn't talk that easily to real people.

LEE Real people talk back.

JORDAN Weird.

RYAN He is a bit of an odd one. 160

LEE A bit?

DREW (*defending Noel*) Hey, if it gets the job done …

NOEL (*ignoring everything else*) So if I had deleted you and tried to cover my tracks, when would I have done it, and where from, which files? 165 (*like a self-pep talk*) Nothing is ever deleted, not really. Nothing disappears, it's just hidden. But not from me, not now. There is always a trace, like breadcrumbs in the forest. *There is always a*

trail, and if there was a trail then it would start 17
… here! (***suddenly excited, clapping***) Yes!

RYAN Have you done it?

NOEL Got it.

DREW Genius!

NOEL BM is not so clever after all. 17

LEE So now what?

NOEL I open them up and re-save them. Shouldn't
take a minute.

FRITH Er … Drew? The car has stopped outside the
office. 18

DREW (***to Noel***) We may not have a minute …

NOEL (***panicking***) I have to have a minute!

FRITH And the driver is getting out and heading for
the door.

DREW (***looking to Ryan***) So much for the simple alarm. 18

RYAN (***with a shrug***) No one's perfect.

DREW (***into the phone***) We need a minute! (***masterfully***)
Do something!

FRITH Do *what*?

DREW Think! 19

LEE (***to Noel***) How will you re-save the files? We
need to take them with us.

NOEL (***pulling something from his pocket***) Memory
stick.

JORDAN (***like it's a really weird thing to do***) Do you *always* 19
have a memory stick with you?

NOEL   (*like it's perfectly normal*) Doesn't everybody?

   Frith talks to a disinterested security guard.

FRITH   (*hastily making things up*) Excuse me … do you
   have the time? Ah, you don't have a watch, but
   no matter, no matter. (*thinks*) I was wondering   200
   … did you know one of the lights on your car
   looked a little … (*acting badly, with exaggerated
   hand gestures*) Was it at the back … Oh no. Now
   that I look, it all seems fine. Sorry for keeping
   you from your work. I'm sure you have lots to   205
   be getting on with. (*after a pause, desperately*)
   Are you nearly finished or just starting? No, I
   don't suppose you have time to stop and chat
   – not to me. Well, you just carry on then. (*Now
   talking so Drew understands*) Yes, you just put   210
   that key in that lock and open the main door
   and step through to the foyer and start shining
   your torch around.

DREW   Is he in?

FRITH   (*into the phone*) He's in. I tried, but I don't think   215
   you have a minute any more.

DREW   (*to Frith*) You did good. (*to Noel*) Are we done?

NOEL   Hold on. (*holding up a hand*) Ten seconds!

DREW   Noel. *Are we done?*

NOEL   (*angrily*) Wait!   220

DREW   (*as calmly as possible*) We have … company!

LEE   (*terrified*) What?

DREW   Security. Coming up!

LEE (*frantic*) When?!

DREW Now. So, Noel, are – we – done?!   22

NOEL We're … (*the whole team hold their breath*) done! Let's go. (*stands, holding the memory stick aloft, beaming*)

LEE (*flustered*) Oh great! What do you mean 'Let's go'? Didn't you hear? Security is coming up   23 the stairs. How are we supposed to get down without him seeing us? (*sits, hopelessly*) We're officially stuffed.

JORDAN (*casually*) Not if we go up.

NOEL (*crumbling*) Oh no.   23

RYAN (*with a smile*) There's always more than one way in, so there's always more than one way out.

JORDAN I'll get you down. Safe and sound. Down is easier than up.

RYAN You'll be fine.   24

NOEL I don't believe this. (*chewing on a fingernail*)

JORDAN You'll have gravity helping you.

NOEL (*putting his face in his hands*) That's what I'm worried about.

JORDAN We have to.   24

RYAN Come on. (*clapping Noel on the shoulder and leading him off*)

> *As they leave, a torch-beam sweeps over where they stood.*
>
> *On the street.*

FRITH Where are they? (*worried*) Where are you? (*looks at the phone*) How does this thing work? (*whispering hoarsely into it*) Hello, hello?! 250

DREW (*emerging, a little proudly*) Hello. Sorry to go silent on you like that, but, you see, I had to cut the call short when I went out (*pointing up*) on that ledge.

FRITH (*disbelieving*) You didn't? 255

LEE (*appears, excited*) We all did. That was fantastic!

FRITH Good for you. Nice work!

NOEL (*walking as if in shock*) Not nice work. It was horrible.

RYAN (*emerging*) You were fine. 260

JORDAN (*appears*) You just kept looking down. I said, 'Don't look down.'

FRITH But you have the files?

NOEL (*happily holding up the memory stick*) If the files are the ones called 'Daedalus Project' then we 265 have the files.

DREW What if the councillor realises that there's been a break-in, and realises that the computer was tampered with? Won't he report it?

FRITH Our Bill is not the kind of person to go to the 270 police – not now, not over this. And it doesn't matter if he knows we're on the case because the fine upstanding citizen is about to be flushed out into the open.

DREW Into a trap? 275

FRITH (*considering the idea*) Maybe. Now … go home and rest. The next few days will test us all to our limits.

NOEL (*holding up the memory stick*) But we need to see what's on these files.

FRITH There's time for that.

NOEL What about tomorrow night? In the situation room.

RYAN & FRITH Situation room?

DREW & LEE Noel's bedroom.

FRITH Good, fine, tomorrow night. Then we see the files …

DREW And set our trap.

Scene Four

In the situation room.

FRITH So now you've seen the files you know
everything. (*drawing a big '£' on the board and
underlining it*) There was more money tied up
in this than you could even imagine. And that's
what Jude stumbled upon, and that's why   5
Jude was pushed that day.

LEE (*angrily*) Jude must have had no idea what was
coming.

DREW (*thinking it through*) So … Jude thought that
Matravers *didn't know* about the Daedalus   10
plans …

LEE … wasn't wrapped up in it all …

NOEL … but needed to know about it?

FRITH Jude had faith in Matravers, and that was his
big mistake.   15

JORDAN (*puzzled*) How much money would it take for
someone to do … that?

RYAN Maybe you need to be a particular sort of
person in the first place.

FRITH (*knowingly*) I think you're right. 20

RYAN Have you made contact to arrange the meeting with Matravers?

DREW (*as if there's something to tell*) Oh yes!

LEE Did you get a response?

DREW (*with a nod of the head*) Oh yes! 25

NOEL We sent them through the PC so it would be easy to save them as evidence.

DREW So I sent: 'Councillor, we need to meet to discuss Jude and Daedalus. Perhaps on the bridge would be good for you?' 30

FRITH (*reading as Matravers*) 'Who is this?'

DREW So I tried: 'That doesn't matter – just be aware that we are on to you. Will you meet or should we take matters into our own hands?'

RYAN Nice. 35

JORDAN Very good.

NOEL But look at this …

FRITH (*as Matravers*) 'Whoever you are, you are playing with fire – I am a powerful man and I can crush you. You don't know what you have got into here 40 – you think you'll bring me down, but I think it might destroy you!'

LEE Do you think you made him cross?

DREW So I wrote: 'Maybe we shouldn't meet then. I won't contact you again.' 45

JORDAN Clever.

NOEL And that calmed him down a bit.

FRITH (*as Matravers*) '**On the bridge, Friday, eight p.m.'**

    Silence for a moment.

NOEL I hope this works.

LEE Me too. It's not as if we have a Plan B.   50

DREW Plan B is to make sure Plan A works, so we have to get this right first time.

LEE If only we had longer to plan and to go through it.

NOEL The files are clear. If we don't do something,   55 and now, then the deal will be done and Matravers will be out of the country in forty-eight hours.

FRITH It's lucky that you came to me in time.

DREW (*apologetically*) Even if we *were* wrong.   60

FRITH You're on the right track now – and I couldn't have done it without you. Maybe we're quits.

DREW Cool. (*to the team*) So do we all understand every part of the trap? It's very complex; lots of things could go wrong *if we don't pay attention* 65 *to the details.*

NOEL We've gone over it all. It all fits into place.

DREW We all know where we're meant to be?

NOEL & JORDAN Yes.

DREW We all know when things start?   70

RYAN & LEE Yes.

DREW We all know what equipment we need?

RYAN   There's a few bits that I need to collect, but I can get everything in town tomorrow.

NOEL   And I need to spend tomorrow making sure I can re-route the security lines and re-allocate the video-feed subsystem. The registry will be tricky, but I just need a little time.

DREW   (*looking blankly*) And for those of us who don't speak 'geek'?

NOEL   (*simplifying*) I just need to do a few things.

LEE   But if it works it will be perfect. Poetic justice!

NOEL   (*looking pleased*) Yeah.

DREW   (*looks doubtful about something*) I still think that on the bridge …

FRITH   (*firmly, but calmly*) No. I'm sure about this. It should be me.

LEE   But maybe a police officer too?

DREW   Maybe we need a back-up plan.

FRITH   No, it must only be me. I want it that way.

NOEL   Why just you?

FRITH   (*mysteriously*) Let's just say that we – me and Bill Matravers – have history.

RYAN   History?

JORDAN   (*keen to hear the story*) What history?

FRITH   (*raising a hand*) Now's not the time. Just trust me; it should be me. It has to be me and just me. (*a new thought*) And, who knows, maybe if I do this then some people in this town might think again about 'the Bird Man'. (*bringing* *himself up to his full height*) Maybe I'll be more than they thought I could be.

DREW   You know it's a risk.

FRITH   (*calmly, firmly*) It's mine to take.

DREW   OK, it's your call. (*to the whole room*) So we're set?   105

FRITH   We should synchronise watches.

RYAN   (*as if it is a stupid suggestion*) Watches?

FRITH   Watches.

RYAN   I don't have a watch.   110

JORDAN   I could synchronise my phone.

LEE   I could synchronise my iPod.

NOEL   (*almost embarrassed*) I have a watch!

DREW   Frith is right, we should synchronise our …

FRITH   (*with irritation*) … our timepieces.   115

DREW   Yeah. In thirty seconds it will be eighteen-hundred hours –

RYAN   (*with a frown*) What-hundred-what?!

LEE   (*patronisingly*) six p.m., Ryan! It means six p.m.!

RYAN   Then just say six p.m.!   120

DREW   (*raising his voice to retain order*) It will be *six p.m.* in exactly fifteen seconds … ten … five … four … three … two … one … *now*.

JORDAN   T minus twenty-four.

FRITH   The game's afoot!   125

DREW   Let's do this!

Scene Five

Drew and Noel are in the situation room. Lee, Ryan and Jordan are at the bottom of the bridge.

DREW   Noel, (*with a sudden lack of confidence*) do you actually think this will work?

NOEL   (*trying to reassure*) It should.

DREW   I've got a bad feeling.

NOEL   We've been through it so many times.   5

DREW   (*putting a hand on his stomach*) But I just feel that …

NOEL   That what?

DREW   Something might go wrong, badly wrong. We're dealing with a killer here. This isn't a   10 game, this isn't TV.

NOEL   I never thought it was.

DREW   (*shaking off the low mood*) Well, it's too late to go back now.

NOEL   Everything and everyone is in place. (*thinks*)   15 Should we have told Frith?

DREW   About …? (*thinks*) Oh no, I still think it's better that Frith doesn't know.

NOEL   Just a few seconds left …

DREW   Showtime. (*into a walkie-talkie*) This is team   20
leader, blue section. Are you there, red section?

LEE   We're here.

DREW   Camera set?

LEE   Set.

DREW   Laptop set?   25

LEE   Set.

DREW   Mobile broadband access set?

LEE   Set.

DREW   (*to Noel*) What was the next question?

NOEL   (*whispers*) Protocols over-ridden.   30

DREW   Protocols over-ridden … set?

LEE   Set. Yes. We're in place, well hidden and
everything is working smoothly. The video
camera is trained on the bridge. Zoom at
maximum, focus sharp and crisp, batteries fully   35
charged. Whatever happens up there, we'll
capture it.

DREW   They should be there any minute.

RYAN   (*looking through binoculars*) We've got
movement. Repeat – we've got movement!   40

JORDAN   (*also looking through binoculars*) Frith is on the
bridge.

DREW   (*apprehensive*) Alone?

JORDAN   Alone so far. Walking to the spot·where we saw
the tracks and found the phone.   45

RYAN (*pointing to the other end of the bridge*) He's not alone any more.

LEE (*whispering urgently*) Suspect is in sight. (*narrating the events*) Suspect is on the bridge. Suspect is approaching Frith. 50

JORDAN Touchdown.

RYAN Contact.

DREW (*to Noel*) OK. We're there.

NOEL (*with relief*) So now we call in the cavalry?

DREW Yeah, let's lift the lid on this. 55

Scene Six

On the bridge, Frith and the councillor meet and look out.

FRITH It's very high up here, isn't it?

COUNCILLOR Great views, don't you think?

FRITH Quite something … yes.

COUNCILLOR You're not *scared*, are you?

FRITH (*with a wry smile*) Actually … strangely … no.   5
I'm not scared at all – are you?

COUNCILLOR Me? Very funny. (*holding his hands out*) Come
on then, let's get down to business. What's this
about?

FRITH 'Get down to business'? What an odd thing to   10
say.

COUNCILLOR (*gruffly*) Business is what I do. It doesn't look
like you'd know much about that though.

FRITH What an interesting sort of person you have
developed into.   15

COUNCILLOR (*ready for an argument*) This is not about me,
this is about you – and, no doubt, something
you either know or think you know.

95

FRITH Oh, I know.

COUNCILLOR Well, (*looking Frith up and down*) either way we'll 20
get it sorted and move on with our busy lives,
shall we?

FRITH Some things can't be easily sorted.

COUNCILLOR Sorting things is what I do – everything can
be sorted. I didn't get to where I am today 25
without knowing that.

FRITH And where exactly are you?

COUNCILLOR Me? Look at me, I'm at the top of the tree, king
of the hill, sitting pretty – I'm just fine. Don't
you worry about me. 30

FRITH But I do … I do.

COUNCILLOR Worry about all the people who want to be me
but aren't.

FRITH But do they know the cost … the high price of
being you? 35

COUNCILLOR (*looking down his nose at Frith*) What rubbish are
you spouting now? What's this about?

FRITH Because there is a price, isn't there? A high
one. One that if you really thought about it
might make you want to pack it all in. 40

COUNCILLOR Trust me –

FRITH (*cutting in*) Trust you?

COUNCILLOR (*ignoring this*) I don't want to pack anything
in. I want to keep on doing exactly what I do,
because what I do makes me very comfortable 45
and extraordinarily rich.

FRITH (*with a sorry shake of the head*) But the price …
the price.

COUNCILLOR (*pointing*) Maybe you're talking about price
because you have one? A price that will help   50
you to forget what you know, a price that will
be more money than you have ever seen. And
all you need to do is … nothing.

FRITH (*looking at the view*) Sometimes doing nothing
is not the right thing to do.   55

COUNCILLOR The right thing? As if there's any such thing
as absolute right or absolute wrong? I mean,
really, is there … isn't there only what you can
get away with?

FRITH Can you get away with murder?   60

COUNCILLOR (*rubbing his hands together*) Ah … like I said …
down to business.

Scene Seven

Drew and Noel are at the police station.

PC LONGMAN (*as if he has already listened to a great deal*)
Listen. I know you two went through a lot. But what you're telling me sounds like the product of an overactive imagination.

DREW (*indignant*) This isn't imaginary. We've worked 5
really hard to get proof, real proof.

PC LONGMAN I think it's just possible that you've been watching a little too much TV.

DREW (*throwing his hands up in frustration*) Why do people always say that? 1●

NOEL You're the last piece of the jigsaw. (*trying to stay calm and reasonable*) We've got everything in line. It's all happening (*points*) out there, now, and all you need to do is get your officers down there. 1●

DREW Just believe us!

PC LONGMAN (*patting Drew on the shoulder*) That might be asking too much.

DREW We've put ourselves on the line for this, we've risked everything – 20

NOEL (*ticking the actions off on his fingers*) We've broken into a house, an office; we've stolen files, phones, SIM cards, video cameras, dongles, hacked into the council's systems – all for this. 25

PC LONGMAN (*takes his hand off, looks at Noel closely*) You've *what*?

DREW Oh, *now* you believe us!

NOEL (*with an open smile*) It's true. I can't lie.

PC LONGMAN So stealing, breaking and entering, and theft of private information? 30

NOEL (*raising a hand*) But it was all to uncover *a worse crime*. And that means it's all right!

PC LONGMAN (*disbelieving*) And this 'worse crime' is a murder? 35

DREW & NOEL Yes.

PC LONGMAN And a massive financial fraud?

DREW & NOEL Yes!

PC LONGMAN By Councillor Matravers?

DREW & NOEL Yes!! 40

PC LONGMAN The very person who set up a fund in Jude's name?

DREW & NOEL (*getting desperate*) Yes!!!

PC LONGMAN (*shaking his head*) It doesn't add up. Doesn't make sense. 45

DREW   Unless you look at it from the councillor's side, unless you want to cover your tracks.

NOEL   Unless getting rid of one little life makes you more money in one day than a police officer could earn in a whole lifetime. 50

DREW   (*whispered*) Nicely said.

NOEL   (*whispered*) Thank you.

PC LONGMAN   (*wavering*) What if you're wrong?

DREW   (*slowly, with great purpose*) What if we're right?

NOEL   (*points to his watch*) It's now or never. 55

DREW   (*seeing that the policeman might help them*) What have you got to lose?

PC LONGMAN   (*gets out a pad*) I might regret saying this, but … OK, you've got ten minutes of my time.

NOEL   Perfect. 60

DREW   We only need five.

Scene Eight

Firth and the councillor are on the bridge.

FRITH   So what do you get out of this?

COUNCILLOR   (*walking away from Frith, spreading an arm to the land below*) Let's think about what this town gets out of this, shall we? Look around you – this is a wasteland, a no-man's land, a piece of   5 worthless scrub. When my plans go through this will be regenerated. (*starts to point to where things will be*) Retail park, leisure centre, hotels, gym, monorail. People coming and going, eating, drinking, staying overnight, buying   10 things in the shops. I'll be bringing people and cash to this area, creating jobs, linking this sorry old town straight to the city. (*stands still and indicates a spot just below them*) And at the heart of this regeneration? A new airport to   15 serve this area.

FRITH   Daedalus?

COUNCILLOR   Reaching for the sky? Nothing wrong with that.

FRITH   So you're doing this for the local people – the   20

101

good councillor serving the community? Let's not look too closely at how cheaply you might have bought this land and how expensively you might sell it.

COUNCILLOR (*with a laugh*) Look all you like – you'll never 25 find anything. You'd have to be a genius to find my name attached to anything, and you don't look like a genius to me. I've spent the past three years making sure that I'm invisible in all of it. That money will go to companies that 30 don't exist, people who don't exist – ghosts and phantoms, which are all actually me. No one will even know it's happened. And the people will love it. (*looking out at the view again*) I've done all right by this place. I was born 35 here, you know.

FRITH (*a bit taken aback*) Oh, *I know* – of course I know.

COUNCILLOR (*curious*) And what is that supposed to mean?

FRITH (*open-mouthed*) You *really* don't *remember* me, do you? 40

COUNCILLOR I remember you. You were the weirdo who caused a fuss at the press launch for my fund. Making a scene at a difficult time. Very improper. But if money is what it takes to sort this, to keep you quiet, then that's fine. Like I 45 said – I just need to know your price.

FRITH (*pointing to his own face*) But you don't know me from before? You really don't? (*looking closely at Matravers*) I used to pass you in the

102

street occasionally and wonder if you were   **50**
pretending – walking straight past. (*turns away*)
I must have changed more than I thought.
The famous sports personality, the gold-
medal winner – I just thought you'd become
too important to talk to. (*a laugh*) But, no, you   **55**
actually had forgotten me!

COUNCILLOR   (*coldly*) I don't know you.

FRITH   (*not looking at Matravers*) I suppose at least
you're happy to do your own dirty work now
… but then it has got dirtier, much dirtier.   **60**

COUNCILLOR   (*as if Frith is talking nonsense*) What are you
talking about?

FRITH   (*still looking out*) I'm talking about a patch of
grass you can almost see from here – just over
there. I'm talking about you and me. We were,   **65**
what, fourteen? fifteen? The fifteen-hundred
metres race, the end of the year – what we had
both worked so hard for.

COUNCILLOR   (*slowly turning to Frith*) What?

FRITH   (*still looking out*) Seems like a lifetime ago   **70**
now – I suppose it is, in a way. (*turning to glare
at Matravers*) You remember, we both knew it
would be close, both knew we stood a chance,
both knew we had a shot at crossing that
line first. And crossing that line first meant so   **75**
much, didn't it? (*with an ironic clasp on his own
shoulder*) But you sorted all that, didn't you?

Had it sewn up before we took a step. You made sure that I could never win.

COUNCILLOR (*disbelieving*) You. 80

FRITH Me. Have I changed that much?

COUNCILLOR (*almost apologetic*) It was never meant to go that far.

FRITH (*almost spitting out the words*) A broken ankle and a busted shoulder is something lots of 85 kids shake off. (*walking around Matravers*) Nothing to make a fuss about … unless you're a promising athlete, unless your future is in your feet, on the track. I said goodbye to that future that day, sat on that track as you sped 90 away and all of your friends, your thugs, made sure I was well out of it.

COUNCILLOR (*unable to look at Frith*) They went too far.

FRITH They did that all right – my ankle never set right. It's always given me pain. And running? 95 That was never an option again; even walking is hard enough. (*close to Matravers*) You never deserved that first place, and I often wonder how many other races you won fairly. I watched your career and thought, 'Did you 100 trample over others too? Did you make your chances better with drugs, with money, with threats, blackmail?' Who knows? You must know.

COUNCILLOR (*suddenly finding strength to look back*) I know 105 that I got my gold, and that is all that matters.

FRITH (*not backing down*) 'I got my gold'? Interesting that you don't say, 'I *won*,' or 'I *earned* my gold'. And, actually, now that we're on the subject – is that all that matters? 110

COUNCILLOR (*again cold and harsh*) Winning matters.

FRITH No matter how …?

COUNCILLOR (*unfeeling*) Winning matters.

FRITH (*pointing to himself*) People matter.

COUNCILLOR Yes. (*pointing to himself*) And I'm 'people'. 115 I matter. My family, my children, they matter – them getting what they want, the best that money can buy, that matters, and that's what they'll get. (*getting agitated*) No one will look down on them! 120

FRITH (*stepping away to look at Matravers*) So easy to see the child in the adult … 'No one will look down on them'? Is that what this is about? Is this where it started, because you were looked down on as a child? (*with a sad shake of the* 125 *head*) Is that really it?

COUNCILLOR (*pointing down to the town*) Those teachers, they looked down on me and I promised myself that I would show them. And that kept me going, on the track, and in my business. I never 130 forgot that promise I made to myself!

Scene Nine

Drew, Noel and PC Longman are at the local CCTV-monitoring station. Lee, Ryan and Jordan are still in position by the bridge.

PC LONGMAN   OK, you're running out of time. You've got one minute to show me something pretty special. And I might be breaking all sorts of rules for even letting you two in here. I could get in trouble. 5

DREW   (*with a smile*) You'll get a medal.

NOEL   (*tapping on a keyboard*) Just watch.

PC LONGMAN   (*looking around at banks of monitors*) And what am I supposed to be watching?

NOEL   Hold on. (*into a walkie-talkie*) This is assistant 10
team-leader, blue section. Come in, red section. Come in.

LEE   We're here. Receiving you, and the bridge, clearly.

NOEL   Time to punch in those codes. 15

RYAN   Punching in. And 'enter'.

JORDAN   We're live.

LEE	Sending live footage via feed now.
JORDAN	Uploading.
NOEL	And …

20

Drew, Noel and PC Longman look up at a screen.

Bingo.

PC LONGMAN (*confused*) What's this? What are we watching?

DREW (*pointing*) That's where Jude was pushed. That's who pushed Jude. That's the man who stood to make a fortune as long as no one stumbled on the Daedalus Plan.

25

PC LONGMAN (*with a little laugh*) The what?

NOEL The plan that Jude found. (*holding up memory stick*) It's all here.

30

PC LONGMAN (*pointing*) So who's *that*?

NOEL That's Frith.

DREW (*with satisfaction*) Frith is part of our team.

PC LONGMAN (*about to leave*) Look, this is all very clever – but as far as I can see this is just two people on a bridge. It's not exactly what I'd call evidence.

35

DREW Then try this (*carefully takes a mobile phone from a briefcase and hands it to the policeman*) – but shhh.

Scene Ten

On the bridge.

FRITH So what will you make out of this: tens of thousands, hundreds of thousands, millions …?

COUNCILLOR (*urgently, jumpy*) Whatever I make, you can have a cut of it, and, trust me, there's enough of it to go round. So you get a percentage to keep your mouth shut. (*rubbing his fingertips together to indicate 'cash'*) That's what this is all about, isn't it? After all your noble talk about winning the right way, doing the right thing, all your griping about losing a race when we were kids … This is where you get to make amends, get even. This is your chance to get back at me by plucking a figure out of the air.

FRITH (*laughing out loud*) My price?

COUNCILLOR (*abruptly*) Name it.

FRITH And if I don't have a price? I'm prepared to bet that Jude didn't have a price. You see I knew Jude. Jude was honest and had humanity. The kind of humanity that wouldn't even leave a bird dying in the street. I suspect it was also the kind of honesty that couldn't be bought. Was that something else that went too far – or was that planned? Did Jude just get in your way? **25**

COUNCILLOR (*refusing to back down*) Jude had a choice.

FRITH Jude was little more than a child. (*a thought*) Did Jude ever tell you why his name, *Jude*, was chosen?

COUNCILLOR What does that matter? **30**

FRITH Jude's mum had miscarriages before Jude was born – they thought they'd never have a child.

COUNCILLOR (*confused*) What?

FRITH (*explaining*) St Jude is the patron saint of hopeless cases. **35**

COUNCILLOR (*mocking, unpleasantly*) Oh, come on.

FRITH (*angering*) That child was wanted … *prayed for*! But none of that matters to you, does it?

COUNCILLOR (*irritated*) That's history! It was not meant to happen, I didn't set out to do it. Things got **40** out of hand. And it doesn't need to happen again –

FRITH (*still angry*) But it could…

COUNCILLOR (*very angrily*) You people!

FRITH (*confused*) Us people? **45**

COUNCILLOR Yes, people like you – you never miss an opportunity to miss an opportunity.

FRITH (*turning away*) Oh, please!

COUNCILLOR (*urgently*) We can settle this. But I suggest you get naming your price quickly. (*after a pause*) Yes, I pushed Jude *and I liked Jude* – so *you* I would happily dispose of, you and your whining and moralising. In my line of business, I can't afford morals.

FRITH But maybe two deaths might begin to look suspicious, mightn't it? (*narrowing his eyes*) Would you get away with it?

COUNCILLOR (*with a laugh and a cruel smile*) I'd be long gone by the time the plods around here even notice anything strange. I'll be sipping fine wine by my pool at my villa in the sun.

FRITH And you won't even notice that … *taint*?

COUNCILLOR (*puzzled*) Taint?

FRITH (*walking around him*) That after-taste when the fine food and expensive wine goes down. What is that …? Tastes of iron … Could it be blood? And when you dive into that pool, what's that face looking up at you – is it Jude, eyes wide, staring?

COUNCILLOR You think I'll beat myself up about this when I'm living it up? You're mad.

FRITH Am I?

COUNCILLOR You see, you're making a classic mistake; you're trying to appeal to my better nature – but what you don't realise is I don't have one.

FRITH (*circling*) But conscience is a strange thing. (***displaying the symptoms***) It might show itself as a stiffness in the shoulders one week, aches and pains the next, and before long you've got ulcers and a heart attack on its way, and why? (***pointing to Matravers's gut***) Guilt, eating away at you from inside, until you're a shell. A hollow shell. And what will you tell those children of yours, when you buy them the pony and the car – all paid for by the taking of a promising young life. Jude, the flyer who never flew, the pilot who never made it to the sky – all in the name of you living it up in the sun!

The councillor grabs Frith by the collar.

COUNCILLOR I'd happily send you down the same way that Jude went. And do you know what? I'd never think of it again! (*coldly*) My conscience won't trouble me. You have a clear choice – you take more money than you've ever seen to keep your mouth shut, or you have an unfortunate fall. (***dragging them closer to the edge***) If I spin it the right way I could even get the stupid people of this town to believe that you threw yourself off after you were riddled with guilt for killing Jude yourself. I'd happily go on the news to tell them (***with mock emotion***) how I tried to stop you, how I came up here to reflect on the life of my poor young employee and found you on the edge. Wouldn't that be

80

85

90

95

100

poetic justice? (*roughly shaking Frith*) So come on, make your choice … (*his face inches from Frith's*) Make your choice! 105

PC LONGMAN (*his voice coming from a phone planted on Frith*) There is another choice, Councillor Matravers.

COUNCILLOR (*shocked, stepping back*) What …! What's that?

FRITH (*taken aback, looking down at himself*) I don't know! 110

COUNCILLOR Have you got a –

FRITH Those kids must have …!

COUNCILLOR (*searching Frith*) What have you done? (*he pulls out the phone and speaks into it*) Who is this? 11

PC LONGMAN This … is one of the local plods, Councillor. One of the people charged with protecting and serving the 'stupid people' of this town.

FRITH (*putting his hands up*) I didn't know! I don't even know how to – 12

COUNCILLOR (*into the phone, thinking fast*) You don't understand, there's been a mistake!

PC LONGMAN You might be right, but perhaps *you* made the mistake, Councillor. And the officers who are on their way to you now will help you clear it up. 12

COUNCILLOR (*trying to keep his cool*) I've been set up! I didn't do it!

PC LONGMAN Didn't do what?

COUNCILLOR I didn't kill Jude!

PC LONGMAN I never said you did. 13

COUNCILLOR (*desperately*) It was an accident!

PC LONGMAN   We'll see. You may be right, you may be telling
the truth. But, you see, apparently everything
you've said and done has been logged and
recorded. It seems you're being filmed by a   135
little camera team from the top of the hill.
(*giving instructions*) Look out in front of you,
and a little to the right … that's it. You are
appearing, right now, in front of my very eyes
on the council's own CCTV system, a system   140
that I seem to remember you had placed in
the town to protect the 'stupid people' from
thieves and murders. (*with a measured tone*)
Maybe it's time to come down, Councillor.

COUNCILLOR   (*stepping to the edge of the bridge*) No. No! I've   145
come too far. This can't be happening! I've
risked everything. (*pointing out to the camera*)
Who are you to try to stop me? I'll have your
job. I'm powerful! I have a say in this town!

PC LONGMAN   I'd love to say it was me, but it seems you've   150
been rumbled by a group of kids. They've got
your files here about this little thing called
the 'Daedalus Project' and we've all watched
the film of you confessing to one murder,
threatening a second and revealing huge   155
fraud, or money-laundering, if you prefer. I'm
not sure what other options you have left.
I've never done this before on the phone, but,
William Matravers, I am arresting you for the
murder of Jude Hill. You do not have to say   160
anything, but anything you do say –

COUNCILLOR (*calling out bitterly from the edge of the bridge*) I have plenty to say!

NOEL (*quietly, up to the screen*) Get back from the edge!

COUNCILLOR I'll have my say!

DREW (*to the PC*) It's not safe up there!

NOEL What's he doing?

DREW (*to Noel*) This is that bad feeling I was talking about!

COUNCILLOR Everyone will hear what I have to say!

FRITH (*grabbing Matravers's shoulder*) Get back, come here!

COUNCILLOR I'm a local hero! (*shrugging Frith off*) People look up to me!

PC LONGMAN Councillor, step back!

LEE (*with disbelief*) What's going on over there?

RYAN (*squinting through the binoculars*) The councillor's freaked out!

COUNCILLOR I am a role model to the people of this town!

JORDAN (*with a shake of the head*) Very unwise, very unwise.

COUNCILLOR You will not destroy my plans!

PC LONGMAN (*urgently, authoritatively*) Step down, Councillor!

COUNCILLOR I've worked too hard for this.

ALL EXCEPT COUNCILLOR Get back!

FRITH Take my hand!

COUNCILLOR (*turning, resentfully*) I don't need your help!

> *The councillor realises he's too close to the edge but it's too late …*

ALL No!

> *A sharp intake of breath from all as the councillor falls. All except Lee turn their faces away.*

LEE (*quietly, sadly*) Icarus. 190

Scene Eleven

Music.

TV REPORTER Many people across the town and country
have expressed shock and surprise at the
new and dramatic events that have unfolded
around the death last month of Jude Hill. It
now appears that a group of young people   5
set about to prove that the death was at the
hands of Jude's employer, Councillor William
Matravers, who in a bizarre twist of fate died
yesterday by falling from the same bridge.

Over recent weeks the young detectives   10
pieced together a case against the local
business tycoon and past sporting hero which
was presented at the scene of the crime. A
struggle took place with another local person,
ending in the councillor falling to an instant 15
death on the very spot where Jude had lain
just weeks earlier.

The police have stated that they are satisfied
that the case against the councillor was
overwhelming, but that they will be seeking to 20

116

interview the councillor's family and a number of his business associates over the coming weeks. They also stated that the team of young people who unearthed the truth displayed bravery and skill to a level that was a credit   25
to themselves, their families, their school and their wider communities.

Now, the sport and weather.

Scene Twelve

Drew and Noel walk onstage, Noel leading.

DREW Where are we going?

NOEL (*friendly, a little joking*) We're not going anywhere – I'm going.

DREW Where are you going?

NOEL I didn't think you'd be interested. 5

DREW (*a little awkwardly*) Well, you see, I thought we might …

NOEL What?

DREW Well … I thought … we could do something together, work out a plan, go to some particular places at a particular time … you know … 10

NOEL Actually, I thought I might just …

DREW Just what?

NOEL Wander. How does that sound? 15

DREW I like to wander, you know I do. (*a pause, a thought*) We made quite a team, didn't we?

NOEL Yes, everybody did their bit.

DREW Yeah.

118

NOEL Look, Drew, are you sure you want to wander – 20
remember what happened last time?

DREW (*playfully*) Last time? (*as if it was all nothing*) Oh,
you mean the whole death-danger-crime-risk-
fear thing?

NOEL Yes. Things like that never used to happen to 25
me in the country. A lot goes on around here,
doesn't it?

DREW Yeah, you never know what's round the corner,
do you?

The boys suddenly stop and look around.

NOEL (*looking off stage*) What was that? 30

DREW (*looking in the same direction*) It didn't sound
good.

NOEL No. No, it didn't.

DREW (*looking to Noel*) Do you want to go and have a
look? 35

NOEL (*unsure and worried*) But … what if … maybe …
we …?

DREW Come on … What's the worst that can happen?

NOEL (*with a frown*) Don't even ask that!

DREW (*pretending to not be interested*) OK, forget it. 40
Let's just walk away, leave it behind. (*walking
away from the sound*) We shouldn't get involved,
best to ignore it. You're probably right.
(*purposefully looking away from Noel*) I mean,
anyway, who wants help out, right wrongs, 45
solve crimes, be held up as a hero …?

> *Drew looks to Noel. After a moment's pause, Noel smiles and runs off towards the sound.*

DREW (*punches the air*) Yes!

> *He runs off after Noel.*

CURTAIN

Crime Scene Investigation

How science can help the police catch a killer

By Cristopher Edge

A dead body is found in suspicious circumstances – what happens next? If you believe some of the cop shows and police dramas on TV, the murder is usually solved by a misfit detective. He will pull back the line of police tape and stomp all over the crime scene in his size twelve shoes. With his eagle eyes and razor-sharp brain, the detective will then find the one vital clue that everyone else has missed. This clue will set him off on a trail that will lead straight to the murderer.

However, in real life, it's not as easy as that. Finding the clues that will help solve a murder means a careful investigation of the crime scene by expert eyes. This is a job for a forensic investigator. A forensic investigator is a detective who uses scientific methods to investigate a crime.

Examining the crime scene

The first thing the police do is ensure the crime scene is sealed off. Using police tape they section off the area where the dead body has been found. This stops anyone from entering the crime scene and keeps evidence from being lost or destroyed.

The crime scene is then photographed to make a record of exactly how it was found. Important details, like the exact position of the body, trails of blood or any signs of a struggle, are noted down. However, other smaller details, like where a half-drunk cup of coffee is placed, are also recorded because this information may turn out to be important later on.

It is vital that the investigators have the most complete picture of the crime scene possible. This will help them as they try to work out exactly what happened. By knowing exact details they can start to piece together the last moments of the murder victim's life.

Searching for evidence

To catch a murderer, the police need to find evidence that will lead them to a suspect. This clue could be a fingerprint, a fragment from a bullet or even a single human hair. Any speck of evidence, no matter how small, can be used to link a suspect to a crime scene.

Although some criminals try to cover their tracks by wiping away their fingerprints or scrubbing away bloodstains with industrial-strength cleaners, a careful forensic investigator can still find the clues that will put the killer in prison. Here are some of the ways investigators uncover hidden evidence:

- **Dusting for fingerprints**: Whenever you touch something, your fingerprints leave tiny traces of grease and sweat behind. Even though these can't be seen by the naked eye, if you wipe dust over them, your fingerprints are then revealed. Investigators can then lift these fingerprints off with a special sticky tape and compare them to their records of known criminals.

- **Finding traces of blood**: Special chemicals can be sprayed to reveal where any bloodstains have been scrubbed away. When lit with an ultraviolet light these chemicals make the bloodstains glow in the dark.

- **Hoovering up the evidence**: Investigators use a special type of vacuum cleaner to collect any tiny pieces of evidence. Dust, hairs and fibres from clothing can be examined under a microscope to reveal important information. Maybe a single thread found at the murder scene matches an item of clothing worn by the killer.

Forensic investigators wear special protective masks, overalls and gloves when gathering evidence. This stops them from contaminating the evidence with their own fingerprints or DNA. Each piece of evidence is sealed in a clear plastic bag and clearly labelled. The evidence bag is then taken back to the lab for further investigation. It can take days to carry out a detailed search of a crime scene and collect all the evidence.

Dealing with DNA

Just like fingerprints can be used to identify a killer, so can the DNA they leave behind. DNA is found in every part of your body – from the hairs on your head to the spit in your mouth! Every person has a different pattern of DNA. The police now collect samples of DNA from people who are suspected of a crime. This means that a single hair found at the scene of the crime can be compared to a suspect's DNA. If the suspect's DNA matches – the police might have found the killer.

Finding the murder weapon

The key part of any murder investigation is to find the weapon. This can give investigators vital evidence. Here are some of the different weapons murderers use and the clues they can give:

- **Guns**: If a murder victim has been shot, the bullet that killed them can give vital clues. The shape of the bullet and the marks on it can help detectives discover exactly which gun fired it. This is because when a gun is fired, it makes a pattern of grooves on the surface of the bullet. If the police find the gun they think was used in the murder, they can fire it again and compare the two bullets. If the marks on the new bullet match those on the fatal bullet, this shows that the gun is the murder weapon.

- **Knives**: The shape and size of a murder victim's wounds can also give clues about the weapon used. A penknife and a kitchen knife would cause very different wounds. Because traces of blood can stick to a knife, investigators can match these to the victim's blood. Killers can also be caught by their fingerprints or traces of their own DNA that they leave on the murder weapon.

- **Poisons**: Some murderers use poisons to kill their victims. This method of murder used to be difficult to detect. Nowadays, however, scientist can detect the smallest trace of poison from a murder victim's blood or urine. This tells the police exactly what type of poison was used and helps them track down where the poison has come from. This can lead them to the murderer.

The next time you turn on a TV police show, watch out for how the detectives solve the crime. See if you can spot how science helps them to catch the killer.

We would like to thank the following schools and students for all their help in developing and trialling *The Death of Jude Hill*.

Little Heath School, Reading:

Marcus Baker

Joshua Baptiste

Chloe Bartlett

Callum Cartwright

Damon Crofts

Bailey Curtis

Marcus Gallaghue

Joshua Morton

Leon Pearson

Lewis Scarrotts

Zoe Vernon - Adams

Matthew Walker